Elias Howe

Inventive Boy

Illustrated by Ann Fleur

Elias Howe

Inventive Boy

By Jean Corcoran

THE **BOBBS-MERRILL** COMPANY, INC.
A SUBSIDIARY OF HOWARD W. SAMS & CO., INC.
Publishers • INDIANAPOLIS • NEW YORK

LIBRARY OF CONGRESS CATALOG CARD NUMBER 62-9255

PRINTED IN THE UNITED STATES OF AMERICA

To those who must sew

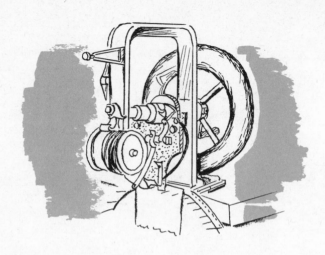

Illustrations

FULL PAGES   PAGE

Elias threw back one of the quilts.   18

They fell and rolled in the snow.   31

They caught up with Sidney's boat.   45

He watched the President down the hall.   85

They looked down into the river valley.   89

He pressed Horace close to his side.   126

"We'll make it out of copper!" he cried.   139

"I've come to say good-by, sir."   164

Elias listened closely to the inventor.   177

They watched Elias sew on his machine.   187

Numerous smaller illustrations

Contents

	PAGE		PAGE
The Surprise	11	The Monkey Chase	100
A Fight	24	Where Is Horace?	114
The Iceboat Race	37	A Gift for Aunt Sarah Ann	131
Ghost in Still Valley	48	A Sailor in the Family	142
Elias Makes Up His Mind	59	Elias Hires Out	154
Elias Meets the President	71	Off to Lowell	169
The Story of Cloth	87	Elias Invents the Sewing Machine	180

⋆ Elias Howe

Inventive Boy

The Surprise

It was a summer evening in 1826. Seven-year-old Elias Howe and his father were talking in the machine shop at their farm near Spencer, Massachusetts.

"I wonder who thinks up all these machines," Elias said.

Mr. Howe smiled. "It makes me happy to see you are interested in machinery, Elias," he said. "I'm afraid you won't be able to do the hard work of a farmer when you grow up."

Elias looked down at his lame leg. He had been born with one leg just a little shorter than the other. He could do almost everything other boys could do, but his father was right—farm work was difficult for a boy who was lame, no matter how much he wanted to help.

"Who *does* think up all of these machines, Father?" Elias asked. He looked at the big saws with their sharp teeth. He looked at the round grindstones that were used to sharpen scissors and knives.

"Inventors think them up, Elias," Mr. Howe said. "Men like your Uncle Tyler and Uncle William." He turned. "Come. We'd better go down to the house. Your Uncle Tyler will be here soon."

Elias' heart leaped with joy. He loved to have Uncle Tyler come. He always brought the most wonderful surprises. Uncle Tyler's last letter said that this time he was bringing a special surprise. A surprise that would completely fill a whole hay wagon!

Elias followed his father out of the machine

shop and along the bank of Cranberry River. He could see his father's gristmill in the valley below. The fading sun shone on the mill's slate roof and cast long shadows at the side.

"Hurry along, Elias," Mr. Howe said, as he strode across the wide pasture.

Suddenly Elias shouted, "There's Uncle Tyler and his wagon now!" He ran past his father, down the sloping pasture hill toward the house. Even his lame leg couldn't slow him when he saw Uncle Tyler.

Elias ran into the barnyard. Big, jolly Uncle Tyler waved and climbed down out of the wagon seat. Elias caught his breath. What could Uncle Tyler have in the wagon? Colorful quilts covered whatever it was.

Elias' mother appeared in the doorway of the big gray farmhouse. Her hair was dark and curly like Elias'. She wore her new white apron. It covered her long dress all the way down to her ankles. "Mercy, Tyler," she said, laughing as she came down the steps, "whatever have you invented this time?"

Elias' father walked into the barnyard before Uncle Tyler could answer. Mr. Howe shook hands with Uncle Tyler. "Glad to see you, Tyler," he said. "How is everything in Boston?"

"Fine," Uncle Tyler boomed. "Brother William sends his love. He is still busy working on that bridge invention."

He turned to Elias. "How are you, my boy?" he asked.

"Fine, Uncle Tyler," Elias said. He looked at the wagon. He could hardly keep from dashing over and pulling the quilts off.

Mrs. Howe smiled. "Elias," she said, "it is suppertime. Run and get Amasa and Mary."

Uncle Tyler saw the disappointment on Elias' face. "Come now, son," he said. "Get your brother and sister. The wagon and what it holds

14

will still be here after supper. This is a surprise which is well worth waiting for."

Elias grinned. He turned and walked around the house, over past the giant elm tree, and toward the orchard. He knew that was where Amasa and Mary were playing. Suddenly he saw Amasa hurrying from behind a gnarled, old apple tree.

"What did Uncle Tyler bring us, Elias?" Amasa called. Amasa was three years older than Elias, and a whole head taller.

"Is it something to eat?" five-year-old Mary shouted. Her red braids flew back as she ran around Amasa and across the clearing to Elias.

"I don't know what Uncle Tyler brought," Elias admitted. "Come see how big it is!"

The children rushed around the house to the barnyard. Breathlessly they looked at the hay wagon with its covering of quilts.

Amasa gave a long low whistle. "This is the

15

biggest surprise that Uncle Tyler has *ever* brought us."

"Take a peek, Elias," Mary begged.

Elias glanced toward the house. Should he take a peek under the quilts? He shook his head. No, that wouldn't be fair. It was Uncle Tyler's right to show them.

"Come, children!" Mrs. Howe called. "Supper is ready now."

The children hurried into the spicy-smelling kitchen. Their father and Uncle Tyler were already sitting at the long wooden table. It was piled high with turkey, and hashed brown potatoes, and hot biscuits that Mrs. Howe had just taken out of the brick oven. There were plates of ripe tomatoes and bright red radishes fresh from the garden.

As soon as the food was being passed, Mary asked curiously, "What did you bring us this time, Uncle Tyler?"

Uncle Tyler smiled. "You'll have to wait until after supper to find out, Mary."

Elias began to eat faster. The sooner he was through, the sooner he would know what the surprise was.

Even Mr. Howe was curious now. "Don't be such a tease, Tyler," he said. "Give us just a little hint."

Uncle Tyler laughed heartily. "All right, I will," he said. He turned to the children. "All I'll tell you is this. You'll never have to use your bed-patter again."

Elias and Amasa stared at each other in surprise. Elias could hardly believe it. *Everyone* had to use a bed-patter. Feather beds needed a good deal of banging and patting to get them back in shape after a night's sleep. Everyone in the Howe house had his own wooden paddle. He used it each morning as soon as he got out of bed.

Elias thought supper would never be over, but at last it was. Everyone hurried out to the barnyard and stood back of the wagon. The early twilight made the quilt-covered present look more mysterious than ever.

"Go ahead, Elias," Uncle Tyler said. "Uncover it."

Elias was so excited. His hand trembled as he threw back a corner of one of the quilts. Then his eyes widened. There was nothing but a mass of wires tied together in a huge frame!

Mrs. Howe was the first to speak. "What *is* it, Tyler?" she asked.

Uncle Tyler's jolly laugh echoed out over the pasture. "It's a bedspring, Polly," he informed her with a wave of his hand.

Mrs. Howe frowned. "You've invented some odd things before, Tyler," she said. "Now you invent a bedspring. What in the world would you use it for?"

"Come along," Uncle Tyler said. "I'll show you."

Uncle Tyler and Mr. Howe carried the strange wired frame into the house. They turned into the boys' bedroom next to the kitchen.

"Have you patented the bedspring yet, Tyler?" Mr. Howe asked, as he and Elias' uncle lifted the feather mattress from the bed.

"I'm going to Washington for the patent soon," Uncle Tyler said.

"What is a patent, Uncle Tyler?" Elias asked with interest.

"Is it something to eat?" Mary asked, interested in food as usual.

Uncle Tyler laughed. "No, Mary. It is a paper an inventor signs saying that he invented something. Then no one else can claim to have invented it first."

The children watched their father and Uncle Tyler lift the bedspring and fit it down into the

20

bedframe. *Crash!* The wire spring fell to the floor. It made a terrible noise.

"Mercy!" Mrs. Howe exclaimed. "The boys will be killed sleeping on that thing."

Uncle Tyler rubbed his forehead. "Guess I didn't make it big enough for this bed." He turned to the boys, looking disappointed. "Looks like you'll have to wait until my next trip to try out the new invention."

Elias looked at the spring unhappily. If only they had something to hold it up. It had to be something wider than the spring.

"Uncle Tyler," he said excitedly, "couldn't we put long strips of board under it to hold it on the frame?"

"Well, blow me down, boy!" Uncle Tyler boomed. "You've got a good thought there." He smiled. "We'll put slats under the spring. You boys run out to the barn. Get me three good-sized strips of wood."

Elias and Amasa rushed out of the room.

Mrs. Howe called after them. "You be careful, Elias. Don't try to carry anything too heavy."

Elias sighed. Mother was always worrying about his lameness. She didn't always understand that being lame wasn't so bad if a boy didn't feel sorry for himself.

The boys lugged the boards back to the bedroom. In just a few minutes Uncle Tyler and Mr. Howe had laid the boards across the bedframe. They put the wire spring on next, then the mattress.

"That will hold it." Uncle Tyler beamed.

Mr. Howe smiled. "You've got real imagination, Elias," he said. "Now I think it is time you children were in bed."

"Come along, Mary," Mrs. Howe said, leading the little girl out of the room.

Elias and Amasa had to be up at five every morning to milk the cows and feed the chickens.

22

Sometimes they begged to stay up a few minutes more. Tonight they said good night right away. They could hardly wait to get undressed and try out the new bedspring.

Quickly the two boys got into their long nightshirts and crawled under the covers.

"Look, Elias," Amasa whispered, "it bounces!"

Elias sat up quickly. He moved up and down. It did bounce! In a few minutes the boys were bouncing merrily.

Mr. Howe spoke sternly from the kitchen. "Boys! That's enough noise. Go to sleep."

The boys hid their heads under the covers. They could hardly stop giggling. Elias was glad Uncle Tyler had brought them his new invention. Bedsprings were fun!

A Fight

ONE WINTER morning Mr. Howe said, "Come home right after school, boys. I want to get the rest of the cards done today. Tomorrow you'll be busy in the iceboat race."

Elias knew that his father was not talking about playing cards. He meant wire brushes. The boys helped Mr. Howe make them by sticking wire teeth into strips of leather. Then Mr. Howe sold the brushes to one of the new textile mills in Lowell. There they were used to comb cotton before it was woven into cloth.

Elias knew that making brushes was important. It was a way of earning money in the winter when farm work was slow. He put a spoonful of corn-meal porridge into his mouth. "All right, Father," he said.

"Elias," Mrs. Howe scolded, "don't talk with your mouth full."

Mr. Howe turned to Amasa.

Amasa nodded. "I'll be home early too, Father," he mumbled.

Elias looked at Amasa with understanding. He knew his brother hated working in the machine shop. Amasa never could understand why Elias enjoyed working around machines.

Suddenly there was the jingle of sleigh bells outside. Elias and Amasa pushed back their chairs and rushed to the door. Even with his lame leg, Elias got there first. He blinked.

White snow covered the whole countryside. Then Elias saw Mr. Peabody sitting in a big sleigh. "It's the snow warden! Hello, Mr. Peabody!" he shouted.

Mr. Peabody waved. He was bundled in a heavy red coat and muffler. "Hurry up, boys!" he called. "I'll give you a ride to school."

Elias nodded. "We'll be there right away, Mr. Peabody!"

The boys hurried across the room for their heavy jackets and knitted caps. They said good-by to their parents and rushed outside.

It was fun riding to school with the snow warden, Elias thought. He knew the snow warden was important in the New England farming country. Everybody used sleds in the winter. Even wagons had long runners on them. A bare place on a snow-covered road meant trouble. No sleds would be able to pass. Mr. Peabody rode around and covered the bare spots with snow.

The boys clambered up into the sleigh. Mr. Peabody clucked to the horses and they moved slowly forward.

"What do you say, boys?" Mr. Peabody said, peering at them from under his bushy eyebrows. "Are you ready to beat that Crockett boy in the iceboat race tomorrow?"

"You bet we're ready, Mr. Peabody!" Elias exclaimed.

This was the first year that he was old enough to enter the iceboat race. He and Amasa had spent the last two weeks getting their iceboat ready for the race. It looked like a sailboat with sled runners.

The race was held on the frozen river, and the winner was given a red sail to show that he was champion. Every boy in town wanted to win that red sail.

Amasa frowned. "I don't know if we can beat Sidney Crockett, Mr. Peabody," he said. "He has won for three years now. Besides, Sidney gets a beautiful new iceboat every year. How can our old one beat his?"

Elias shook his head. "You give up too easily, Amasa," he said. "You can't win by giving up."

Mr. Peabody laughed. "I like your spirit, Elias," he said. "I'll be at Cranberry River tomorrow cheering for you and Amasa."

He slapped the reins lightly against his horses. They broke into a trot. Before long, the sleigh pulled up in front of the small, one-room, red schoolhouse.

"Thank you, Mr. Peabody," the boys said, as they climbed out of the sleigh.

"Any time, boys." Mr. Peabody smiled. "See you tomorrow at the race."

The boys nodded. They waved good-by to the snow warden.

"Look there, Elias," Amasa whispered as they turned into the schoolyard.

Elias looked across the clearing. A group of boys were crowding around Sidney Crockett. Sidney was a tall boy of thirteen. Elias knew this was Sidney's last year of school. In 1826, New England farm boys went to school only until they were fourteen.

Amasa frowned. "I bet Sidney is still bragging about winning the red sail for three years in a row. He's that kind."

Elias nodded. Sidney *did* brag a lot, Elias thought. In fact he bragged all the time. No one dared say anything about it, though. Everyone knew Sidney was a bully.

Sidney turned. "Here come those Howe boys now," he said in a loud voice.

He swaggered over to Elias. "Listen, Elias," he said, "you better stop telling everyone that you and your brother are going to win the race. It's only going to make you look sillier than ever when you lose it."

Elias stood as straight as he could. He barely came to Sidney's shoulder. "We think we *can* win, Sidney," he said.

Sidney hooted. "Your brother only came in third last year. This year he'll probably come in last. Especially with nobody but a lame one like you along to help him!"

Elias doubled his hands into fists. Before he could make a move, Amasa leaped at Sidney. They fell to the ground and rolled over and over in the snow. The crowd of boys around them shouted with excitement.

"Boys!"

Sidney and Amasa scrambled to their feet. Mr. McGraw, the schoolmaster, was standing in the school doorway. He was scowling over his glasses.

Elias hurried forward. "Don't blame Amasa for fighting, Mr. McGraw," he said. "He was doing it for me."

Mr. McGraw looked sternly at Elias. Then he turned to the two bigger boys. "Who started the trouble?"

"*He* did!" Sidney pointed at Amasa.

"That's not true!" Elias exclaimed.

Mr. McGraw looked at Amasa. "Did you hit Sidney first?"

Amasa nodded.

Mr. McGraw shook his head sadly. "Boys, how many times have I told you that fist fighting settles nothing?" He turned to Amasa. "Your punishment will be to stay after school. You will clean the slates and stack the books."

Elias looked at Amasa. Father would be very angry with him. Amasa had been told to come right home after school to help with the brushes.

Quickly Elias stepped forward. "Please, sir," he said. "May I stay and help Amasa?"

Mr. McGraw's forehead wrinkled in surprise. "You want to stay after school?"

Elias swallowed. Of course he didn't want to stay after school. He just didn't want his brother to take the blame alone.

Mr. McGraw shrugged. "All right, Elias," he said, "you can stay."

He turned to the grinning Sidney. "For your part in this, Sidney," he said, "you can wear the dunce cap this morning."

Sidney's grin faded quickly as the group of boys in the schoolyard shouted with laughter. Mr. McGraw glared at the boys. They fell silent and followed him into the schoolroom.

Rows of hard benches lined the room. The boys hung their coats and hats on the hooks in the walls. Jostling and pushing, they took their seats and opened their books. They tried not to giggle when they looked at Sidney. He sat on a high stool in the corner wearing a tall dunce cap.

Elias had a hard time studying his lessons. He was thinking about the brushes that were supposed to be done today. What if his father made him and Amasa stay home tomorrow to do them? They would miss the race!

Elias looked at Sidney. Sidney would tell everyone the Howe boys were afraid of losing, and that was why they didn't come to the race.

"Elias," Mr. McGraw said sternly, "keep your eyes on your book."

The day seemed to drag on forever. After school it took a long while to clean all the slates and stack all the books. At last it was finished and they were free to go home.

Elias and Amasa put on their coats and hats. They said good night to Mr. McGraw.

Suddenly Mr. McGraw smiled. "Good luck in the race tomorrow, boys," he said. "Now run along home."

Elias grinned at Mr. McGraw. He hurried out the door after Amasa. They trudged down the snow-covered road.

"It must be nearly suppertime," Amasa said worriedly. "What will we tell Father?"

"Guess we'll have to tell him the truth," Elias

said unhappily. He knew his father wouldn't like their being kept after school.

The boys rounded a bend in the road. They could see their house up ahead. Elias saw a man walking toward them. It looked like—like Father! "Father must be very angry about our coming home late," Elias thought. "Why else would he come looking for us?"

The boys hurried forward. Now Elias saw his father looked more worried than angry.

"Are you boys all right?" Mr. Howe asked.

"Yes, Father," they said.

Then one word tumbled out after the other as together they told him what had happened.

"I see," Mr. Howe said. He looked thoughtful for a moment. "Mr. McGraw was right of course. Fist fighting is not the way to settle an argument."

He put an arm around each boy's shoulder and said, "Come, boys, we'll do the brushes later. Right now we had better go to the machine shop and check your iceboat. *This* year the Howe boys are going to win that red sail!"

Elias saw that Amasa still didn't look as if he thought they could beat Sidney and his new iceboat with their old boat.

As they walked up over the hill to the machine shop, Elias began to wonder. Was Amasa right? Was Sidney's new boat too fast for their old boat to beat?

Well, Elias thought, maybe they couldn't get a new boat, but he had a plan he was *sure* would make their old boat go faster. He'd been thinking about it for a long time. Maybe Father would let him try it!

The Iceboat Race

A few minutes later, in the machine shop, Mr. Howe looked at the iceboat.

"The boards seem good and strong," he said. He ran his hand over the boat.

"I've cleaned the runners," said Amasa. "They're as smooth as butter. The sails are just the right size too."

Elias said nothing. He was busy looking at the tiller, a piece of wood at the back of the boat. The tiller was attached to the rudder and was used for steering.

"Father," Elias said, "wouldn't it be better if the tiller and rudder were in front? Then we would go faster. We wouldn't have to twist and turn to see where we're going."

"Elias," Amasa said, "the wind is too strong and cold to face when we're sailing. It would blind us."

Mr. Howe nodded. "Amasa is right," he said. "It is a strong blast of air."

"Well," Elias said excitedly, "I've thought and thought about it. Maybe I could build a low wooden shield and put it on the front of the boat. We could lie down on the deck and look over it. I'm sure we could borrow some glasses from Mr. Wooley the blacksmith to protect our eyes from the blinding cold."

Mr. Howe frowned thoughtfully. "You mean the goggles he uses when he forges metal?"

Elias nodded.

Just then Mary poked her red head through the doorway. "Mother wants you to come to supper," she said.

"All right, Mary," Mr. Howe said. "Tell her we'll be right there."

Turning back to Elias, he said softly, "That is an unusual idea you have, son. Iceboats have always had their tiller and rudder in the back. There is no doubt the boat would go faster with them in the front."

Suddenly he smiled. "We'll try it! After supper, Elias, you can build the shield. Amasa can get the goggles."

He walked toward the door. "Come along to supper now."

The boys followed their father to the house. All through supper they talked excitedly about the new kind of iceboat they would have. After he finished eating, Elias hurried back to the machine shop. Happily he sawed a low wooden shield the width of the boat. He hammered it to the boat front. Then he took the tiller and rudder from the back and screwed them to the front of

39

the boat. Last of all, he screwed the rudder to the front runner.

Elias rose to his feet. Now they would be able to steer the boat easily! He could hardly wait to try it out tomorrow! He turned and made his way out of the machine shop and back to the house. Amasa had already come back wih the big, funny-looking goggles that tied on around their heads. The boys tried them on.

Mother and Mary laughed. "You look like big frogs," Mary said with a giggle.

Mr. Howe smiled. "Off to bed now. The race starts at eight in the morning. You will have your chores to do first."

The next morning Elias and his brother hurried through their breakfast and chores. Then they pushed their iceboat out of the machine shop and down the snowy slope to the frozen Cranberry River.

"Look at the crowd!" Elias exclaimed. He

40

looked around at the many people who had come to see the race. Everyone seemed to be shouting happily to one another through the frosty air.

There were at least eleven other iceboats crowding the riverbank. Boys were everywhere, raising sails, polishing runners, and looking over every inch of their boats before the race started.

Elias noticed that there were many people standing around one boat. It was a shiny new one with very big sails. "That must be Sidney's boat," Elias thought.

Suddenly he saw Sidney coming through the crowd toward him. Sidney was followed by a group of boys.

"Hey!" Sidney shouted. "Look at the boat the Howe boys are using. It's made backward. That's a good joke!"

Sidney leaned down and poked at the tiller. He doubled up with laughter.

Elias felt his face flush. Then he thought of

what Uncle Tyler had told him. Folks often laugh at new ideas.

"Go ahead and laugh at our boat, Sidney," he said. "You still have to beat us."

Amasa stepped forward. "That's right!"

"Anyone could beat that silly-looking thing." Scowling, Sidney turned and walked back to his own shiny new iceboat.

All but one boy tagged along behind Sidney. The boy looked about eight years old. Elias had never seen him before.

"Hi!" Elias said.

The boy's freckled face broke into a smile. "Hi!" he said, walking over to Elias. "My name is George Fisher. We just moved into the farm next to yours."

"You mean where Mrs. Flint lives?" Elias asked curiously.

George nodded. "She's my aunt. I'm going to live with her." He looked at their boat with interest. "I've never seen an iceboat before." Elias and Amasa were surprised at this.

"Really?" Elias said. "I thought everyone went iceboating."

George smiled. "Not in Virginia they don't. That's where we come from."

"Attention!"

The boys turned at the sound of the loud voice. It was Mr. Kent, the race starter. Mr. Kent stood at the far end of the river. He talked through a big megaphone.

"All racers line up at the starting line! When I call 'Go,' push off, This is a half-mile race. GOOD LUCK!"

"Hurry up, Elias," Amasa shouted, as he pushed the boat across the slick ice to the starting line.

Elias hesitated. He could see by the look on George's face that he would like to go along with them.

"Come on, George," Elias said. "You can ride with us."

"Honest?" George's freckled face beamed.

Elias grinned at his new friend and led the way across the ice. Amasa stood at the back of the boat ready to push off. The eleven other boats were lined up and ready. Elias tied on his glasses and lay down on the flat deck. George sprawled out beside him.

"Ready! Go!" Mr. Kent called.

With quick running steps, Amasa pushed the boat forward. As it gained speed, Amasa leaped on deck.

Away they went across the ice! Elias gripped the tiller and kept the boat steady with the wind. Amasa was ready to man the sails. They could hear the crowd shouting from the shore.

They passed boat after boat. Then they caught up with Sidney's boat. They were going to pass it.

"Hey, Sidney!" Elias shouted, as their boat sped past the big new one.

"We're ahead!" Amasa shouted. "Keep the tiller steady, Elias."

Elias' heart leaped. They were coming to the bend in the river. They would have to sail it into the wind. If they made it around the bend they would win the race. Elias' hand tightened on the tiller. If only they could do it without tipping over!

"Loosen the sails, Amasa!" Elias yelled. He pulled the tiller to the right and headed straight into the wind.

Quickly Amasa loosened the sails so they wouldn't fill with wind and drive the boat backward. Elias and George pressed against the deck. They felt the front of the boat push against the strong wind.

"The winner!"

Elias could hardly believe it. They were over

the finish line. He let his hand fall from the tiller. Amasa pulled down the sails.

Everyone ran across the ice to congratulate them on their victory.

"The red sail is yours, boys," Mr. Kent said, handing Elias the prize.

Sidney came hurrying toward them. He bent down, staring at their boat.

Sidney looked puzzled. "I don't see how a funny-looking boat like that won," he said.

"It just looks funny because it's different," Elias said. "Maybe someday many iceboats will have their tiller in the front."

Later, as Elias and Amasa walked home with George, Amasa laughed. "I guess we took the wind out of Sidney's sails," he said.

Elias grinned. "Guess we did," he agreed. He wasn't really thinking about Sidney, though. He was thinking of how much fun it was to invent new ways of making things.

Ghost in
Still Valley

It was a bright sunny day in April, 1827. Elias and his good friend George sat on the low stone wall surrounding the Howe family's cornfields. They were watching Elias' father pushing a wooden, horse-drawn plow.

Amasa walked in front of the plow. He held the horse's reins and guided the animal very carefully. It was important that the plow turn the dirt over evenly.

Elias sighed. "I wish I could help plow," he said wistfully.

George looked surprised. "I thought you didn't like farm work."

"I don't," Elias admitted. "I don't want to get out of it just because I'm lame, though. Father says plowing is too hard for me." He shook his head. "When I grow up, I'm *never* going to let being lame stop me from working hard and— and doing important things!"

Suddenly the boys heard the *rat-tat-tat* of a drum in the distance.

"It's the peddler!" Elias cried.

They jumped down from the wall and rushed out to the lane. Elias saw the peddler's bright red-and-blue, horse-drawn wagon coming up the road. The little gray-haired peddler sat upon the high seat up front. He was banging on a toy drum to let everyone know he was coming. He stopped his drumming as he drew near the boys. Now they could hear tinware rattling around inside the wagon.

Elias jumped up and down with excitement. "Hello, Mr. Peddler!" he shouted.

The peddler pulled his horse to a stop. He grinned down at Elias. "Is your ma home, young man?" he asked.

Elias nodded. "Don't go away!" he yelled. He raced up over the hill toward the house.

A minute later Elias burst into the kitchen. "Mother! The peddler is here!" he cried.

"Mercy, Elias!" his mother exclaimed as she hurried from the bedroom. "Stop all that noise! You'll frighten Horace. I just sent Mary berry-picking so she wouldn't wake him."

Sometimes it was hard to remember they had a new baby. "Sorry," Elias whispered.

"You don't have to whisper either, Elias," Mrs. Howe said, laughing. She stooped down by the fireplace and picked up a blanket that was tied at the top.

Elias knew that the blanket held homemade candles and bags of chicken feathers. His mother would trade these for pins and needles. He hoped his mother would get some red-striped candy canes in the trade, too!

Elias heard the peddler's wagon rumble into the barnyard. He helped his mother carry the blanket outside.

"Afternoon, ma'am," the peddler said. He climbed down from the wagon and hurried around to open the rear doors.

Elias and George watched wide-eyed as the doors fell open with a jingling and a rattling. They stepped forward to feast their eyes on what the wagon held. They saw brightly decorated salt and pepper shakers, dried codfish hanging from the ceiling, cheese, tinsmith's tools, and bottles of red-striped candy canes!

Mrs. Howe spread her blanket on the ground. "I'll trade half a dozen bags of chicken feathers and two dozen candles for a dozen packages of pins and needles. A large bottle of candy canes, too," she added, smiling.

"A fair trade," the peddler agreed. He took the candles and bags of feathers and tucked them into his wagon. Then he climbed up into the wagon and handed out the pins, needles, and candy to Mrs. Howe.

As the old man climbed down again, he carried a bright new teakettle. "Have you ever

seen a finer piece of tinware?" he proudly asked Mrs. Howe.

Mrs. Howe studied the shiny kettle. "It's very nice," she said.

"The finest you'll find this side of Boston," the peddler boasted. "The price for you, ma'am, is only—" he paused—"one silver dollar!"

Mrs. Howe laughed. "No, thank you. Elias has made me a kettle that looks as bright and shiny as the one you hold in your hand."

Elias flushed with pride.

The peddler chuckled. "Don't go fooling me, ma'am," he said. "There isn't a boy alive who could make a teakettle as fine as this."

George spoke up. "Elias can. Show him, Elias. Show him the fine, shiny teakettle you made for your ma all by yourself!"

Elias looked at his mother. She nodded. He ran to the kitchen for the teakettle. "Maybe I can't plow," he thought, "but I can use a soldering iron and a hammer and pot metal to make a teapot."

The peddler's eyes widened in surprise when Elias returned with the teakettle. The man ran his hand over the tin. "There isn't a crooked seam in it," he murmured. "I wouldn't have believed it if I hadn't seen it!"

Mrs. Howe stepped forward. She took her teakettle. "Have you time to come in for a cup of tea?" she asked.

"I'd like that, ma'am." The man smiled.

Elias and George led him into the kitchen. They sat down at the table while Mrs. Howe made the tea. George leaned toward Elias and whispered, "Ask him to tell us a story."

Elias' eyes sparkled with excitement. Peddlers told the best tales in the world!

"A story?" the peddler said, when Elias asked him. "All right. This one is true. In fact it happened just today."

54

Mrs. Howe served the tea and then hurried away to take care of Horace. The boys sat on the edge of their chairs. They didn't want to miss a word the old man said!

The peddler sipped his tea. He looked at the boys mysteriously. "Do you know Still Valley?" he asked softly.

"That's where the old Indian burial ground is, isn't it?" Elias asked. "The one about a half-mile from here?"

The peddler's voice was almost a whisper. "That's the place."

George shivered. "Some people say it's haunted. They say that ghosts of dead Indians walk that valley."

"Yes," the peddler said. "It started with the Indians of long ago. They thought the valley was a sacred place. No one was allowed near the big rocky hill in the middle of the valley because that was the burial ground."

The little old man paused to take another sip of tea. The boys hardly breathed as they waited for him to go on with his tale.

"No one was allowed near that hill," he continued. "Not even relatives of the people who were buried there. The Indians said that if you walked on the graves, the dead Indians would rise to haunt you."

The peddler leaned close to the boys. "Today," he said softly, his eyes narrowed, "I drove my wagon up over that hill to save time. Suddenly I saw a rock as big as a pineapple swaying back and forth all by itself! I stopped to look at it. It moved even faster. I couldn't get away quick enough!"

"Really?" Elias' eyes were big. "The rock really moved?"

"Do you know what *I* think was pushing that rock?" the peddler said.

"A—a ghost?" George stammered.

"Yes," the old man said. He rose to his feet. "That is *just* what I think. A ghost was warning me to go away."

The boys sat in silence. They stared at him.

"It can't be!" Elias burst out. "There is no such thing as a ghost!"

The peddler's face was serious as he walked to the door. "Don't be so sure, lad," he said. "I saw that rock moving with my own eyes. Next time I'll take the long way round."

He pause in the doorway. "Thank your ma for the tea. I must be off now." With a wave of his hand he hurried outside.

Elias and George walked slowly to the door. They watched the peddler drive his wagon out of the barnyard. The boys did not say a word until the wagon had disappeared down the road. Then George whispered, "My aunt says that not even a tree will grow in Still Valley. Don't you think that's strange, Elias?"

Elias frowned thoughtfully. "Maybe the soil isn't rich enough," he said.

"Maybe there really *are* ghosts in Still Valley," George said. "Maybe they won't *let* anything grow there."

How could that be? Elias wondered. He just *had* to find out.

"George," Elias said, trying to sound as if he was not afraid, "let's go to Still Valley. Let's see if the peddler was telling the truth about the rock moving around."

George looked uncertain. "Well, all right," he said at last. "I—I'll follow you."

"All right," Elias agreed. He hoped he looked braver than he felt as he led the way over the green meadows toward Still Valley.

Elias Makes Up His Mind

FIFTEEN MINUTES later, Elias and George stood at the top of a slope leading into Still Valley. The valley below was rocky and full of shadows. There was an eerie look over everything.

"It sure is spooky," George said. "I'm afraid to go any farther."

Elias took a deep breath. "Come on," he said. He led the way down.

The boys felt a chill breeze when they reached the rocky valley road. Elias' feet seemed to drag. Nevertheless, he forced himself to hurry forward. They came to the end of the road. Elias pointed ahead. "There's Still Hill. That's the old Indian burial ground." His voice sent echoes through the silence.

George looked up at the high rocky hill before them. "L-let's go home," he pleaded.

"You can go if you want to," Elias said. "I'm going to climb that hill."

George glanced around. He didn't want to go back alone. He followed Elias up the hill.

Elias looked about carefully as they climbed. There were many rocks, but none of them were moving. Elias grinned. "See, George," he said. "The peddler was just making up a story."

George sighed with relief. "I guess he was."

Suddenly his eyes widened. He pointed upward, speechless with fright.

Elias looked up the hill. He saw a rock moving back and forth! The rock was as big as a pineapple! The peddler had been telling the truth after all!

George turned and raced back down to the

foot of the hill. Elias turned to follow him, but then he stopped. He just *had* to know *what* was making that rock move, even if it turned out to be a ghost.

Frightened, Elias bent down and picked up a long, stout stick. Slowly he climbed up the hill. He crept nearer and nearer to the rock. At last he could reach it with his stick. His hand trembled and his heart pounded, but he leaned forward and pushed it over.

Elias swallowed hard. There was a hole under the rock. Something was moving in it! His heart pounded. He crept over and peered down into the hole. What he saw made him shout with laughter—and relief.

"What is it, Elias?" George called weakly. "What do you see?"

Elias turned and waved. "Come up and look for yourself."

Slowly George came up the hill. He knelt by

Elias and looked into the hole. "Why, it's nothing but a groundhog!" he exclaimed. "*He* was the one pushing the rock!"

Elias laughed. "Of course! Somehow the rock must have rolled down over his hole. He sleeps underground all winter. Now that it's spring he wanted to come out of his hole."

The little groundhog's sleepy eyes seemed to wink at the boys. Then he jumped out of his hole and ran away up the hill.

The boys laughed about the "ghost rock" all the way home.

"Just the same," George said, as they reached his farm. "Still Valley is a pretty spooky place, whether it has ghosts or not."

"It sure is," Elias agreed. He said good-by to George and started off for home.

A few minutes later, Elias walked up the lane toward his house. He saw his father sitting under the big elm. Mr. Howe was talking to a tall thin man. As Elias came nearer he saw the man was Uncle William Howe.

Suddenly Elias felt someone grab him from behind. The next thing he knew he was lying on the ground. A blond boy of about eight was sitting on his chest. Elias blinked. It was his cousin Nat Banks.

"Nat!" Elias laughed. "Get off me!"

Nat swung to his feet. He grinned down at Elias. "Surprised to see me?" he asked.

Elias got to his feet. He threw his arm around Nat's shoulder. "You bet I am! What kind of trick was that, though—jumping out at me and knocking me down?"

"That was to pay you back for the last time I was here," Nat said, as they walked toward the men. "Remember how you dropped out of the elm tree and scared me?"

Elias laughed. "I remember," he said.

The boys reached Uncle William and Mr.

Howe. Uncle William's thin face broke into a smile. "How have you been, Elias?"

"Just fine, Uncle William."

Elias and Nat sat down on the grass beside the men. Elias listened with interest. They were talking about the bridge Uncle William was inventing. Uncle William called it a "truss bridge." He explained that his idea was to tie big fat logs together with forged metal to hold the bridge up. He called them girders.

"Yes," Uncle William finished, "my bridge is coming along nicely. There are just a few things to improve on it. It shouldn't be long before I can think about patenting it."

Mr. Howe looked thoughtful. "You really think we'll need bigger and stronger bridges for these trains you were telling me about earlier? Do you think it will be soon?"

Uncle William leaned forward. "I tell you," he said, "I'm sure of it. The first railroad in the

United States was built just last year in Quincy, Massachusetts. Before you know it, railroads will be built all over the country."

Elias' dark eyes were bright with excitement. "We learned about that in school, Uncle William," he exclaimed. "Our schoolmaster told us that the first railroad—one with raised track with wheels fitting onto the track—was built by the Quincy Railroad. It was called the Granite Line. It was built in 1826 to bring granite for the Bunker Hill Monument from the quarry to a wharf on the Neponset River. He said they used horses to pull the train."

Nat nodded. "Uncle William says that someday trains will use steam to make them go. These trains will be able to travel everywhere."

Uncle William turned to Mr. Howe. "It's true," he said. "When trains use steam they *will* go everywhere. That means we'll need strong bridges to carry the trains safely over big rivers.

That's why I think my truss bridge will be important to America's future railroads."

Mr. Howe chuckled. "You don't have to prove it to me, Will," he said. "An inventor like yourself is a man of vision."

Elias frowned. "What is a man of vision, Father?"

Mr. Howe paused to light his pipe. "Well, Elias," he said slowly, "a man of vision knows that the work he does today is important to the kind of tomorrow we will have."

Elias thought about what his father had said. "I think I understand."

Mr. Howe waved his pipe. "Now you and Nat run along," he said pleasantly. "Supper will be ready soon. You won't have much more time to play."

The boys pushed to their feet. They walked across the barnyard. They were still thinking about what Father and Uncle Will had said.

"Let's go find Amasa," Nat said as they reached the barn.

"Maybe he's in here," Elias said, sticking his head in the barn doorway. "Amasa!" he shouted. "Are you in there?"

There was no answer. Elias and Nat started to walk away, but then they heard a rustling noise in the barn hayloft.

"He's hiding in the hay," Nat whispered.

The boys crept over to the loft ladder. They listened. Someone was up there!

Elias jumped suddenly as he heard Amasa yell, "Man the topsails!"

Elias and Nat scrambled up the ladder. They saw Amasa standing on a wide board. The board was surrounded by hay.

"Why didn't you answer us, Amasa?" Elias demanded.

"Because I'm playing 'sailor in the hay.'" How could I answer you when I'm a hundred

miles out to sea?" Amasa looked at the hay around Elias' feet and added, "You're standing in the ocean, Elias."

Quickly Elias and Nat leaped onto Amasa's board. They sat down and watched Amasa pull up make-believe sails. They listened to him shout orders to his imaginary crew. Then he sat down beside Nat.

"Do you want to be a sailor when you grow up?" Nat asked him.

"More than anything!" Amasa exclaimed. "That's *all* I want to do!"

"I want to be a government worker," Nat said. "Maybe I'll be a governor. What do you want to be when you grow up, Elias?"

Elias frowned. He hadn't made up his mind yet, though he had thought about it a lot. " I guess I like working with machinery best," he was thinking now. "I like studying up new and better ways to make things work, too, like inventors do."

Elias sat up straight. "I want to be an inventor," he said. "I'd like to invent a machine that will help people."

The boys stared at him.

"What kind of machine?" Nat asked.

"I don't know yet," Elias admitted.

"Boys!" Mr. Howe's voice came floating across the yard. "Supper is ready!"

Nat and Amasa climbed down from the loft. Elias followed softly. He felt a special kind of excitement. "Maybe when I grow up," he thought, "I really *can* make a machine that has never been made before."

Elias Meets
the President

ONE MORNING in October, Elias stood by the kitchen table. He watched his mother pack a suitcase. His dark eyes were sparkling with excitement. Now that he was nine, he was going on a business trip with his father. They were going to the Lowell, Massachusetts, textile mill where cloth was made.

"Elias," Mrs. Howe said, "hand me that nightshirt from the chair."

Elias handed his mother the nightshirt. "Have you ever been to the Lowell textile mill?" he asked eagerly.

Mrs. Howe snapped the suitcase shut. "No,

son," she said pleasantly. "Selling the wire brushes to Mr. Rose is your father's job."

"Is Mr. Rose the man who runs the mill?"

"Yes." Mrs. Howe put the suitcase down by Elias. "You can take this now. Everything you'll need is in there."

"Mother," Elias said excitedly, "do you think Mr. Rose will let me look at the machines that make cloth?"

Mrs. Howe ruffled her son's dark hair. "I'm sure he will," she said with a laugh. "Now run along. Your father is waiting in the wagon out front. It will take a day and a half to get to Lowell. Father doesn't want to waste any time in getting started."

Elias gave his mother a hug. He picked up the suitcase and hurried out the door. The October air was crisp with early frost. "Winter will be here soon," Elias thought, walking over to the wagon.

"All ready?" Mr. Howe asked. He reached down and took the suitcase from Elias.

"All ready," Elias said happily. He climbed up beside his father.

Mr. Howe put the suitcase behind the wagon seat. He clucked to the two horses. Slowly the horses pulled the wagon out of the barnyard and down the lane.

Elias could hardly sit still. He felt wonderful! He was going to see all kinds of new machinery in the textile mill!

The wagon rumbled out onto the main road. The road was covered with crushed rock.

"Beautiful country, isn't it?" Mr. Howe said. He puffed gently on his pipe.

The horses trotted along at a steady pace.

"Yes, Father," Elias said. He looked at the curving hills and winding valleys veined by little streams. Trees bordered the road, their leaves bright with the red and gold and orange colors of autumn. Now they were passing the Jenks Inn. Stagecoaches filled the yard.

"Did I ever tell you," Mr. Howe said, "that George Washington visited Spencer once? He stayed in that very inn."

Impressed, Elias looked back at the inn. "Really?" he said. "Did they have a post office at the inn as they do now?"

"No," Mr. Howe said. "It wasn't until 1789 that folks around here had a post office."

"How did people send letters?" Elias asked.

Mr. Howe was silent for a minute. "Well," he said at last, "folks around here say that it was Hero who carried the mail."

Elias' face brightened with interest. "Who was Hero, Father?"

Mr. Howe's gray eyes twinkled. "A dog," he answered.

"A *dog* carried the mail!"

"That's what folks say." Mr. Howe smiled.

"A man named Henshaw owned and trained the dog to carry mail. People attached letters to Hero's collar. Then the dog traveled fifty-two miles to Boston and left the letters at the post office there. He returned with any messages the postmaster at the Boston post office attached to his collar."

Elias thought, "A dog as postman! What a funny sight that must have been!"

Then he laughed. "Father, I wonder if, instead of signs warning the postman, 'Beware of dog,' folks put out signs for Hero saying, 'Beware of people.'"

Mr. Howe laughed with Elias.

Soon Elias forgot all about Hero. He was too busy looking around at all the new sights.

At noon, they stopped under a tree. They ate the sandwiches Mrs. Howe had packed for them. Then once again they started off down the road. Elias began to feel sleepy.

The next thing he knew his father was shaking him awake. "I must have fallen asleep," Elias thought with surprise. He shivered. The sun had faded and the air was turning cold.

"It will be dark soon," Mr. Howe said. "We'll stop at the Red Brick Inn overnight. It's just around the next turn."

Elias was wide-awake now. He had never stayed in an inn overnight before. The wagon creaked around the turn. Elias saw the inn. It was very big and was built of red brick. A fancy sign hung out in front which read THE RED BRICK INN.

Mr. Howe guided the horses into the inn's courtyard. Elias saw there were many stage-coaches here.

"I hope there is a room left," Mr. Howe said worriedly. "The next inn is five miles down the road. It will be dark soon, and the horses are tired."

"They are hungry too, I bet," Elias said, knowing how hungry *he* was.

A short man with white hair came out of the inn. He hurried over to the wagon to greet the new arrivals.

"Welcome to Red Brick Inn," he said heartily. "I'm Mr. August, the innkeeper."

Mr. Howe leaned down from the wagon. He shook hands with Mr. August. "I was afraid you might be out of rooms."

"You're very lucky, sir," Mr. August said. "There is just one room left." He lowered his voice. "These stagecoaches belong to government people. They are traveling with the President. He is due here any minute."

Elias' eyes widened. "You mean the *President of the United States?*"

Mr. August straightened his shoulders proudly. "Yes," he said. "President John Quincy Adams has chosen *my* inn in which to spend the night."

"A great honor for you, Mr. August," Mr. Howe said. He climbed down from the wagon. "My son and I would like a little supper. Would you see that our horses are taken care of?"

"Of course, sir," the innkeeper said. He called to the stable boy to unhitch the horses. Then he led the way into the inn.

"How beautiful it is," Elias thought. He stood in the big hallway and looked up at the crystal chandeliers hanging from the high ceiling, gleaming with soft light. A long, winding stairway, red carpeted, wound upward at the left.

Mr. August nodded toward the dining room off the hall. "Go right in, sir," he said. "Supper is being served. When you wish to go to bed, your room is at the top of the stairs to the left."

"Thank you, Mr. August," Mr. Howe said.

The smiling innkeeper hurried away to take care of his many duties before the arrival of the President.

Elias and his father ate a hearty supper of roast veal and baked potatoes. Elias kept his gaze on the dining room door while they were eating. "I wouldn't want to miss the President!" he thought.

Mr. Howe looked toward the door every now and then too. Then, as Elias was finishing his dessert of baked apple, Mr. Howe drank his coffee, then stood up.

"I'm sorry, Elias," he said. "I'm afraid the President has been delayed. We'll be leaving here before the sun rises in the morning. We still have many miles to travel, and my meeting with Mr. Rose is at noon."

Elias looked up quickly. Did his father mean it was bedtime already? "Father," he exclaimed, "we'll miss seeing the President if we go right up to bed now!"

Mr. Howe hesitated. Elias noticed how weary his father looked. "He has driven many long miles today," Elias thought. "He must be very, very tired."

"All right, Father."

Elias rose to his feet, followed Mr. Howe out of the dining room and up to bed.

Mr. Howe went right to sleep, but Elias lay awake a long time. He listened for the President's coach. All he heard was the whisper of the wind through the treetops. Then, just as he was about to give up and go to sleep, he heard another kind of sound. The wheels of a stage-coach were grinding over the crushed rock of the road leading into the courtyard.

Elias sat up and listened. The coach was turning into the courtyard! Quietly, so as not to awaken his father, he slipped out of bed. He hurried across the room and looked out the window at the scene below.

Elias saw an elegant gentleman step out of the coach into the light of the courtyard. Now the innkeeper came into sight. He was bowing and smiling. Elias saw him lead the gentleman into the inn.

Elias dashed to the door and out into the hallway. He tiptoed down the hall to the head of the stairs. He peeked over the railing post. He could hear the men talking, but he couldn't see any of them yet.

"Would you care for a little supper, Mr. President?" he heard the innkeeper ask.

"It *is* the President," Elias thought. "If only I could see him!"

He pushed further over the rail. His feet were off the floor. He peered down. Now he could see the President. How handsome he was in his black suit and lacy white shirt!

"No, thank you, Mr. August," the President was saying in his deep voice. "I am much too tired to eat any supper. I think I'll go right on up to bed."

"He's coming up the stairs," Elias thought. "I've got to get to my room!" He tried to pull himself back over the rail. He seemed to be stuck. Then he realized that his nightshirt was caught on the railing post!

The President was almost at the top of the stairs now. There was nothing Elias could do. He was fairly hanging on the stairpost. How *silly* he felt as the President stopped and stared at him!

"What have we here?" the President said.

"H-how do you do, sir," Elias said, twisting and turning, trying to free himself.

Suddenly the President began to laugh. Elias flushed. He'd never thought he'd meet the President of the United States like this!

Still laughing, the President reached out and freed Elias. He lifted him down.

"I'm sorry I laughed," the President said. "However, I'm grateful to you, son. When I arrived tonight, I was so tired I thought I'd never laugh again."

Elias smiled weakly. "Thank you, sir."

"Come!" President John Quincy Adams said. "I'll walk you to your room. You can tell me what you're doing here."

As they walked, Elias told the President that he was going to Lowell to see some wonderful new machinery.

The President's face was serious again by the time they reached Elias' room. "Yes, son," he said, "it looks as though the machine age is here. It is indeed a most exciting time for our country —and an exciting time to be alive."

Elias' heart pounded. Even the President of the United States thought that machines were exciting!

The President shook hands with Elias. "Goodby," he said. "Remember not to lose your interest in machinery. In the years to come our country will need men who can build new and better machines."

"I'll remember, sir," Elias said.

In his nightshirt he stood and watched the President as he walked down the hall and entered his room.

Elias went back into his bedroom. As he closed the door, his father suddenly sat up in bed. "Who is that?" Mr. Howe said.

"It's me, Father." Elias rushed across the room. One word tumbled out over the other as he told about meeting the President.

"That's a memory you'll treasure, Elias," Mr. Howe said, as Elias slipped back into bed. "You must tell your friends and Amasa all about it. Go to sleep now—it's late."

Elias snuggled down under the covers. His eyes felt heavy with sleep and he was very tired. "Father," he murmured.

"Yes."

"Do I have to tell them at home that I met the President while I was hanging on a stairpost in my nightshirt?"

Mr. Howe smiled in the dark. "No, Elias," he said. "That will be *our* secret."

Elias sighed happily. A minute later he was fast asleep.

The Story
of Cloth

MR. HOWE and Elias continued on to Lowell bright and early the next morning. The horses traveled along at a brisk pace. It seemed no time at all before Mr. Howe said, "We'll be in Lowell soon, Elias."

Elias could hardly wait to get to the textile mill. "Does it take lots and lots of machines to make cloth, Father?" he asked.

"Not too many, Elias," Mr. Howe answered. "There are really only three steps in the making of cloth."

"Three?"

"Yes," Mr. Howe said. "First, the cotton is

harvested and the seeds are taken out. Then the cotton is sent to the mill where it is combed and twisted into threads."

"I bet I know what the third step is!" Elias cried. "Weaving the threads into cloth!"

Mr. Howe laughed. "That's right. Of course, sewing the cloth is a fourth step. There isn't any machine for that, though, up to this time." He looked ahead, squinting. "Looks as though we are coming into Lowell now."

Elias leaned forward excitedly. They were going up a very high hill. When they reached the top, Mr. Howe pulled the horses to a stop. He and Elias sat looking down at the river valley below them.

"There is Lowell," said Mr. Howe. "Since the mills were started in 1822, it has grown steadily. I think that one day it might be America's most important textile center."

Elias' eyes were wide with wonder. He had

never seen a place like this before. Rivers and narrow canals and huge grassy plots of land criss-crossed through the valley. Hills surrounded it. Looking into the distance, he could see the peaks of the New Hampshire mountains.

"Where is the mill, Father?" he asked, anxious to get into the mill itself.

Mr. Howe started the horses slowly down-ward. "We have to cross that bridge at the bottom of this hill. Then you will see the mill, Elias. It is right near a big waterfall."

A minute later they crossed the bridge. Elias looked along the curving line of the river. "I see it!" he shouted and pointed to a giant waterfall at the far end of the river. On the riverbank was the mill. It was a big wooden building with a huge waterwheel on the side. Two more mills were being built close by.

Mr. Howe reined his horses to a stop in front of a small house near the mill. "This is Mr. Rose's office," he said. He helped Elias climb down from the wagon.

The door of the office opened. A red-faced man peered out. His shirtsleeves were rolled up. "Hello there, Mr. Howe!" he said. "Step right in. I've been expecting you."

"Mr. Rose, this is my son Elias," Mr. Howe said, as they stepped into the office. They were in a big room which was crowded with desks. Many men worked at the desks, which were covered with important-looking papers.

"Please sit down," Mr. Rose said.

A young man of about sixteen poked his head through the open doorway. "Dad," he called, "a new shipment of cotton just came in. Do you want it put into the breaker-picker?"

Elias thought, "I wonder what a breaker-picker is."

"Yes, Frank," Mr. Rose said. "First, come in and meet Mr. Howe and his son Elias."

Smiling, the tall young man came into the office. He shook hands with Elias and his father. "Are you interested in how we make cloth, Elias?" he asked pleasantly.

"Oh, yes!" Elias exclaimed.

Mr. Rose walked around to his chair behind one of the desks. "Frank," he said, "Mr. Howe and I have business to talk over. Why not take Elias along and show him the mill?"

"Good idea, Dad—" Frank smiled at Elias— "if Elias wants to."

Elias nodded excitedly.

"Fine," Frank said, walking to the door. "Come along then."

As they entered the mill, Frank pointed to a huge metal tank close by. "This is the breaker-picker," he said. The mill was a very noisy place. Frank had to shout to make himself heard over the roar of the machinery.

Elias noticed big bundles of cotton standing

by the tank. "They must weigh five hundred pounds each," Elias thought.

"Paul!" Frank called to a fat man. "Dad says to start the cotton through."

"All right, Frank," the man replied.

"What does the breaker-picker do?" Elias asked curiously.

"Well," Frank said. "The machinery inside the tank tears the cotton apart. Air blows through the cotton and takes out the dirt. Then the cotton goes through rollers. The rollers flatten out the cotton."

"You mean that one machine does all that!" Elias marveled.

"Yes," Frank said. "Next, the cotton goes through the carding machine. Come, I'll show it to you."

"I want to see that," Elias said eagerly. "My brother and I help our father make the wire brushes for it."

"Really?" Frank led the way to the big machine next to the breaker-picker tank.

Now Elias saw the cotton going into the carding machine. Then it went through more rollers. On the rollers were the wire brushes that he and Amasa helped make at home. The brushes went round and round. They brushed the cotton free of snarls. Next, the cotton went through a pair of smaller rollers. From them it came out looking like soft rope.

"That's wonderful!" Elias exclaimed. "What happens to the cotton next?"

"It goes through a machine that stretches it, then twists it into thread. Then the thread is put on the weaving loom. Come along, I'll show you the loom."

A minute later Elias stood before a huge weaving loom. He saw that cotton threads were stretched from the top of the loom to the bottom. A boy was busily putting spools of thread into a container. The container looked like a big hollow needle.

"What is that?" Elias asked, pointing to the needlelike container.

"That's a shuttle," Frank explained. "The spools of thread are called bobbins. The bobbins are put into the shuttle. Then the shuttle weaves threads over and under the threads on the loom."

Elias stood and watched the loom weaving cloth. The needlelike shuttle slid back and forth almost faster than he could see. First one way, then the other, the big needle darted. The cloth grew longer and longer.

The sudden clanging of a bell made Elias jump in surprise.

Frank laughed heartily. "That's the lunch bell," he explained.

The roar of the machines stopped. Frank said, "The men have turned off the machines. After they eat lunch they will start them up again.

Come along, we'll go back to the office and eat with your dad and mine."

Elias and Frank entered the office. Mr. Howe and Mr. Rose had finished talking over their business. Mr. Rose had a large boxed lunch. He passed around sandwiches and a piece of pie. The men drank coffee; the boys, milk.

"What did you think of our mill, Elias?" Mr. Rose asked.

"I thought it was wonderful," Elias said. He took a bite of his sandwich. "I liked the loom best. I liked watching the needle move back and forth."

His father nodded. "Yes, son. I'm not surprised that you did. That is a very interesting machine," he said. "They call the needle a 'fly shuttle' because it moves so fast."

"Who invented clothmaking machines, anyway?" Elias asked.

Mr. Rose answered. "Such men as Hargreaves, Arkwright, and Crompton. They were all English inventors."

"It was only thirty-eight years ago that *America* learned how to build these machines," Mr. Howe said.

"Really?" Elias said. "Why did it take us so long to learn?"

Mr. Rose smiled at Elias' puzzled look. "It was because of the English clothmakers. They tried to keep their machines from leaving England. How the machines were made was kept a big secret too."

"How did we find out how to make them?" Elias wanted to know. "Did we send spies over to England?"

"No." Frank laughed. "Samuel Salter was the first man to teach us. He worked in an English cotton mill from the time he was fourteen. He left England in 1789 and came to America. He carried pictures of the machines in his mind. In

America he built copies from memory. That was the start of the clothmaking industry in this country."

"Lucky for us that Slater came to our country," Mr. Rose said. "It was hard work making cloth at home."

Mr. Howe nodded. "It certainly was. My mother worked for weeks and weeks on a hand loom making cloth for our clothes. Now, if someone would invent a sewing machine, we wouldn't have to sew the cloth by hand either."

Mr. Rose laughed. "I think that's expecting *too* much, Mr. Howe."

Elias' eyes flashed. "A sewing machine! I think that's a wonderful idea, Father!"

"An impossible one, probably," Mr. Howe said. "Men have already tried to build such a machine. Their machines have only succeeded in tearing the cloth."

"Maybe someday an inventor *will* think of a

successful way to build a sewing machine," Elias insisted.

"Maybe," Mr. Howe agreed. "However, right now we'd better start toward home."

Mr. Howe and Elias said good-by to Mr. Rose and his son. They walked out to the wagon.

"Thank you for showing me the clothmaking machines, Frank," Elias said.

He and his father climbed into the wagon.

"I hope you'll come and see them again, Elias," Frank said.

A few minutes later the wagon rumbled over the bridge. Elias looked back at the mill. "Someday, Father," he said, "I'd like to come back to Lowell. I'd like to watch the shuttle weaving cloth again."

Mr. Howe puffed on his pipe. "Maybe someday you will, son," he said. "Maybe someday you will."

The Monkey Chase

SCREECH! Elias ran the last of the knife blades across the coarse grindstone. Then he laid the knife beside the others he had just finished sharpening for his mother.

He felt a little sorry that they were all done. He liked holding the blade carefully against the sharpening machine. He liked watching the grindstone make the knife edge look new and shiny again.

Suddenly Elias remembered his jackknife. "That hasn't been sharpened in a long time," he thought. "I'd better do it now too."

Just as he took the jackknife from his pocket,

the door of the machine shop burst open. Amasa and Mary and George rushed in.

"For goodness' sake, Elias," Mary exclaimed, "come on! We'll miss the fair! It's only going to be here for one night, you know!"

"Yes," Amasa said. "We'd better hurry. We have to be home before ten o'clock."

The fair! Elias had been so interested in sharpening the knives that he'd almost forgotten about it.

"I'm almost ready," he said. "I just have to sharpen my jackknife."

"Never mind that, Elias," Amasa said impatiently. "We haven't time."

"Sure we do," Elias said, as he sharpened the jackknife. "No sense in not finishing what you start. There! It's done." He held the knife up to the light, snapped the blade shut, and slipped the knife into his pocket.

"You'd better put your jacket on," Mary said.

"Mother says these fall nights can turn surprisingly chilly."

"All right, Mary." Elias smiled at his sister. She always tried to sound like Mother. He guessed it made her feel grown-up.

Elias took his jacket from the wall hook and followed the other children out of the machine shop and on through the barnyard.

From the top of the hill they could see the lights of the fair booths down in the vacant lot by the town square.

As they walked, Mary chatted happily. "A girl I know told me that they have the most beautiful handiwork in a tent at the fair. She said that Mrs. Jenks made a doily that won a blue ribbon. I can hardly wait to see it. Maybe I'll learn how to make one just like it and give it to Mother for Christmas."

"Who cares about doilies?" Amasa snorted. "*I'm* going to the game booth. Maybe I'll play darts and win a prize." A longing look came into his eyes. "Last year they had a model ship I would have given anything to win."

"They are going to have fireworks at the fair this year," George said. "I know what I'm going to do first, though. I'm going to watch the monkey do tricks."

Elias looked at his friend with interest. "What monkey?" he asked.

"Haven't you heard?" George said. "There's a hurdy-gurdy man at the fair. He has a monkey on a rope. When the man plays his music box the monkey dances. He does tricks too."

"Really?" Elias exclaimed. "I would sure like to see that happen. I've never ever *seen* a monkey before."

"Neither have I," George admitted.

"I saw a picture of one," Amasa said. "It was a drawing in one of my schoolbooks."

The children hurried around the bend in the

road. The town square was crowded with people strolling into the fairgrounds.

"Listen!" George said, as they joined the excited crowd. "The hurdy-gurdy man is playing his music box."

Elias nodded. He could hear the gay tinkling tune. It sounded as though it was coming from over by the lemonade booth.

"Well, I don't care about any old monkey," Mary said. "I'm going over to the cake booth where Mother is. She said that after she was through selling cakes she would take me over to see Mrs. Hunter's prize-winning doily at the handiwork booth."

The boys hardly noticed that Mary had left them. They were anxious to see the monkey. When they arrived at the lemonade booth the crowd was so thick they could hardly push their way through.

Suddenly the crowd roared with laughter.

"What is the monkey doing?" Elias shouted to George over the noise.

"I don't know," George shouted back. "I can't see over all these people."

Little by little the boys pushed forward. At last they stood in front of the crowd.

Elias' eyes grew round with wonder when he saw the monkey on the rope. "He is so tiny!" Elias thought. He'd always imagined that monkeys were *big* with long, long arms.

The hurdy-gurdy man was short and fat. He had a curly black mustache. He wore a green hat with a red feather in it. Elias laughed when he saw that the little monkey wore a green hat with a red feather in it too.

"Look what the monkey is doing now!" Amasa yelled.

The crowd howled with laughter. The monkey was standing on his toes and dancing to the music of the hurdy-gurdy man. The man's face

beamed as he turned the handle of the square
box on wheels that made the music.

Then he held up his hand for silence. "Now,
folks, you see Jocko do the greatest trick of all."
He took off the monkey's hat and unhooked the
rope from its collar.

"Stand on head, Jocko!" he ordered.

The monkey put his palms flat on the ground.

106

He flipped up onto his head. He pushed with his hands and began twirling around.

"How funny he looks!" Elias thought. "Just like a spinning top with legs."

The boys laughed and laughed.

Then abruptly from behind them there came a blast of noise. The darkening sky lighted up with a blaze of color.

"The fireworks!" the crowd yelled. They all turned and rushed toward the other side of the fairgrounds.

Elias, George, and Amasa turned to join them, but a shout from the hurdy-gurdy man made them turn back.

"Jocko! Jocko!" the man shrieked.

"Look!" Elias yelled. "The fireworks frightened the monkey. He's running away!"

Like a flash the monkey scampered across the fairgrounds. Between people's legs he darted. Up over the display booths and around the handiwork tent he ran. Then he disappeared from sight.

"Jocko! Jocko!" the hurdy-gurdy man shouted. He ran after the monkey as fast as his short fat legs would carry him.

Elias and the other boys wove in and out of the crowd, trying to keep up with the excited owner of the monkey.

Now everybody was looking up.

"There he is!" a tall man shouted.

"Where? Where?" people asked.

"Up there!" The man pointed to the top of the handiwork tent. "He seems to be caught in one of the ropes that holds the tent up."

"Look!" a little old lady screamed. "The rope has slid up around his neck. The poor thing will be choked to death!"

Elias' throat tightened. "Why doesn't someone *do* something?" he thought.

Almost as if in answer to Elias' thoughts, a

young man appeared with a ladder which he leaned against the side of the tent.

Then he turned to the crowd. "We'll need somebody who doesn't weigh too much to climb up there. It's a pretty strong tent, but it just might collapse if someone were to put too much weight against it."

Elias looked up at Jocko. The monkey whimpered and tried to free his head. Elias swallowed hard. He *had* to get Jocko down!

"I'll go!" he shouted. He ran forward.

"Wait, Elias!" Amasa called. "It's much too dangerous!"

Elias paid no attention. Before anyone could stop him, he was up the ladder. He crawled across the roof of the tent toward the monkey. His heart pounded as he felt the canvas sway, but he moved slowly forward. He heard the crowd below breathe a sigh of relief when at last he reached the monkey.

"Easy, Jocko," Elias said soothingly. He tried to lift the rope from around the trapped animal's neck, but couldn't do it. The rope was all tangled. How could he get it free? he wondered.

Then he thought of his jackknife. Of course! He could *cut* the rope. He was glad he had taken time to sharpen the knife!

The monkey whimpered. He reached out his arm to Elias.

"It's all right, Jocko," Elias said softly. "I'm going to set you free."

He slipped his jackknife from his pocket and leaned over. Carefully he moved the sharp knife back and forth, back and forth. There! The rope was cut!

"I'll have to be extra careful going back down," Elias thought. "Other ropes are holding the tent up, too, but with one rope cut the tent might fall in."

Elias tried not to think about it. He took the

110

scared little monkey by the hand. Carefully he worked his way back to the ladder, pulling the monkey after him. Then he put one arm around the animal and, with his other hand holding tightly to the ladder, climbed to the ground.

Everyone rushed toward him. "Good work, boy," they shouted.

The hurdy-gurdy man threw his arms around the boy and the monkey.

"You are hero! I reward you! I hear friends call you 'Elias.' Jocko no more named 'Jocko.' He now named 'Elias the Monkey'!"

The crowd cheered.

Elias' face turned red. "Shucks, I'm not a hero," he said. He pulled away from the man's arms and handed him the monkey.

The little animal snuggled down against the hurdy-gurdy man's chest.

Elias gave the monkey a pat on the head. Then he hurried away to Amasa and George.

"Come on," Elias said to them. "Let's go play that game of darts."

"Let's," George agreed.

The boys hurried across the lot to the booth for their game.

"You were right about finishing what you start, Elias," Amasa said thoughtfully. "Just think of what would have happened to that monkey if your jackknife hadn't been sharp enough to cut the rope."

"Yes," George said. "By the time someone had got a knife up to you, that monkey might have really been choked by those ropes."

Elias laughed.

"What's funny?" the boys asked him.

"I was just wondering," he said, "how Jocko is going to feel being called 'Elias the Monkey' from now on."

"He probably won't answer to it at first," said George, with a grin.

"That's true," Elias said.

"I'll bet having a monkey named after you is the strangest reward a boy ever had," Amasa said, laughing.

Elias answered, "Maybe it is a strange reward, but I don't mind at all giving my name to a nice little monkey like Jocko." Then he smiled. "That's not his name anymore though, is it? I meant a nice little monkey like *Elias!*"

The three boys shouted with laughter.

"You're the best sport in the world, Elias," George gasped. "You can even laugh at a joke on yourself."

Where Is Horace?

IT WAS a spring morning a year later. Elias was ten years old. He lay in bed for a while, listening to the noises out in the kitchen. He could hear Aunt Sarah Ann Howe humming a gay tune. He could hear his mother grinding the coffee for breakfast.

"It's fun having Aunt Sarah Ann here," Elias thought. "She knows so many new games and jokes!" He threw back the covers and jumped out of bed.

As Elias dressed he thought of Mr. Haydon. Mr. Haydon was the man Aunt Sarah Ann was going to marry next month. She had brought

114

him from Worcester last week to meet the family. All the Howes liked Mr. Haydon. "I'm glad they bought that farm down the road from us," Elias thought happily.

"Elias," Mrs. Howe called from the kitchen, "hurry out and eat your breakfast. Your father wants you and Amasa to go and meet the mail coach this morning."

"I'm coming," Elias answered. He hurried into the kitchen. The family was already sitting down to breakfast.

Elias patted two-year-old Horace's head as he passed his high chair. He peeked in at baby Juliette sleeping in a cradle near by.

"Hurry up, Elias," Amasa said. He reached past Mary for a piece of bread. "Father wants us to go down to Jenks Inn and wait for the mail coach."

Elias sat down at the table. He smiled across at Aunt Sarah Ann. He noticed her blush when

Mr. Haydon asked her to pour his coffee. "How pretty she is," Elias thought.

"Did you hear me, Elias?" Amasa asked.

"Yes," Elias answered. "You don't think I'd forget the new plow is coming today!"

Mr. Howe's eyes twinkled. "Still interested in this new kind of plow, son?"

"Sure!" Elias said, passing the butter to his mother. "I bet we'll be the first farmers in the *country* to have a cast-iron plow!"

Mr. Howe laughed. "I wouldn't say that, Elias. The cast-iron plow was invented back in 1819. The seat and wheels on the plow are what's new. Now we farmers won't have to walk and push our plows. We'll be able to ride."

"I'll be able to help plow too!" Elias exclaimed. "My lame leg won't matter if I can ride on the plow."

"That's right, Elias," his father said. "Your lame leg won't matter one bit!" He shook his

116

head. "I'll have to put the plow together myself though. It comes in three parts."

Elias' dark eyes sparkled. "Can I help put it together?"

"We'll see," Mr. Howe said.

Aunt Sarah Ann dimpled. "Mr. Haydon would help you," she said, "only we *do* have to start back to Worcester this morning. We still have wedding plans to make."

"That's right," Mr. Haydon said. He took a gold watch from his vest pocket. "We must leave very soon now."

Elias knew that they were getting married in Worcester. Mr. Haydon said his parents were too old to come all the way to Spencer. After the wedding they were moving into the farm down the road.

Elias took one last swallow of milk. He stood up. "Let's go, Amasa," he said. "I promised George we would call for him."

Mary jumped to her feet. "Can I go with the boys, Mother?"

Her mother shook her head. "Not now, Mary. I want you to take care of Horace. Maybe later you can take him for a walk down to the inn."

"All right, Mother," Mary said. She reached for a biscuit.

Amasa got to his feet. He gave Mary's red pigtail a pull. "You'll be big as a cow if you don't stop eating so much," he teased.

Mary tossed her head and took a big bite of the biscuit.

"Remember, boys," Mr. Howe said, "tell the coach driver to leave the plow parts at the inn. I'll pick them up later today."

The boys nodded to their father and hurried on out the door.

They called for George and walked over to Jenks Inn. They saw stagecoaches lined up in the courtyard. They looked at each coach carefully. None of them had a government seal on the door.

"I guess the mail coach hasn't come in yet," Elias said.

"I wonder where all these coaches are going," Amasa said.

"I know what!" George cried. "Let's play Where Are You Going, Sir?"

"Let's!" Elias exclaimed.

For the next half-hour the boys watched the people who went in and out of the inn. They took turns guessing who they were and where they were going. George and Amasa agreed that Elias thought up the funniest answers.

The sun was high in the sky now. It was getting very hot. Elias looked at the huge maple tree growing by the side of the inn.

"Wish we could sit in the shade," he said.

George's eyes widened. "You mean under *that* tree?"

119

"Well, it's the only tree around," Elias said, a little impatiently.

"You know we can't sit under that tree, Elias," Amasa said matter-of-factly. "The wolf-dog would surely get us."

Elias looked at the huge tree. The trunk of the tree had a hole in its side. The hole was so big that three men could hide in it. Mr. Jenks kept a mean dog chained to the tree. The dog used the hole for his house.

Elias thought, "No one would dare rob Mr. Jenks with a dog like that around." Elias knew that some people said it wasn't a dog at all. They said it was a wolf!

He wondered where the dog was today. Maybe he was on the other side of the tree. The trunk was so big you had to walk around it to see the other side.

"It's too hot to stand here anymore," Elias said. "I'm going over and see if the dog is still chained there. If he is gone, we can sit under the tree."

Elias walked slowly toward the tree. He could see the long chain attached through the big hole in the trunk. Carefully he tiptoed around the tree trunk. He saw the big hairy dog, asleep. "He does look like a wolf," Elias thought. The sleeping dog's long sharp teeth pushed out from between his lips.

Elias shivered and stepped back. He hurried over to George and Amasa. "The dog is there all right. Sound asleep, though."

"Elias!"

The boys turned at the sound of Mary's voice. She held little Horace by the hand. Elias wasn't surprised to see that Mary was eating a big fried chicken leg.

"Has the coach come yet?" Mary asked. She let go of Horace's hand.

Happily Horace sat down in the dirt.

"No, the coach hasn't come," Elias said. He smiled at Horace, who was sifting dirt through his fingers.

"There it is now!" George shouted excitedly. "There's the mail coach!"

The children ran to the road. They saw the mail coach turn into the innyard. Strapped to the back of the coach was a wooden crate. Amasa pointed to it. "I bet that's the plow!"

The coach driver heard Amasa. "Are you waiting for this-here plow?" he asked.

"Yes," Elias said. "My father wants you to leave it here at the inn. He will come by soon to pick it up."

"All right," the coachman said. He climbed down from his high seat. The children stared up at him. He was the biggest, tallest man they had ever seen!

"He must be *seven feet* tall," George whispered to Elias.

"He's big, all right," Elias agreed. They followed the man around to the back of the coach
where the crate was fastened on.

Mary nibbled on her chicken leg. She followed the boys. They watched the big man un-
strap the crate and hoist it onto his shoulder. He
carried it over to the inn wall.

"Wasn't it heavy?" Elias asked, as the man laid the box down.

"Not very," the man said with a grin. "You youngsters run along home now. Tell your father his plow is here."

"We will," Amasa said. "Thank you for bringing it."

"You're welcome," the man said, smiling. He waved and disappeared into the inn.

"Come on, Mary," Elias said. He and the other boys started out of the courtyard.

Mary didn't answer.

Elias turned back. He saw Mary staring at the spot where Horace had been playing.

"Horace is gone!" Mary squealed.

Elias' heart pounded. No one had been paying any attention to Horace. They had been too busy with the plow.

"What if he went down to the river?" Mary whispered. "He'll be drowned!"

124

"We'll find him," Amasa said. "He's too little to have gone far."

The children looked all around the inn yard. They ran past the sleeping dog and down to the river. They hunted through the fields. They hurried back to the inn and searched through the stagecoaches. Horace was nowhere in sight.

"He—he's gone!" Mary sobbed. "We'll never see him again."

Elias thought hard. Where would Horace go? He was too small to walk very far. Elias looked around slowly. All at once he noticed the big maple tree by the inn.

"The hole in the tree!" he shouted. "Maybe that's where he is!"

"Oh, Elias," Mary cried, "go see, quick! If the wolf-dog wakes up, he'll bite Horace!"

Elias ran to the tree. He bent down and stepped into the hollow trunk. It was dark inside. At first he couldn't see anything. Then he saw

125

Horace. The little boy lay back in the corner sleeping peacefully.

Elias gently shook his little brother. "Horace," he whispered, "we're going home now."

Horace opened his eyes sleepily. He saw Elias. His chubby face broke into a grin.

Elias gently helped Horace to his feet. Suddenly he stiffened with fright. Mary was screaming something about the wolf-dog.

Now he heard Amasa's voice. "Don't move, Elias!" his brother called. "The dog is awake. You'll never make it out of there. I'll get Mr. Jenks to come out here."

Elias pressed little Horace close to his side. "What if Mr. Jenks doesn't get here in time?" he thought. "What if the wolf-dog attacks us?"

Elias took a deep breath. "Mary," he shouted quickly, "throw the dog your chicken leg!"

A second later he heard Mary's voice. "He's got it, Elias."

Quick as a flash Elias and Horace ran out of the tree. They ran across the yard to the other children.

George grabbed Elias' arm. "Weren't you scared to death, Elias?"

Elias smiled weakly. "I sure *was!*"

Amasa took Horace's hand. "Come on, everybody," he said. "Let's go home."

Mary started to cry.

"*Now* what's the matter?" Amasa demanded.

"I—I thought the wolf-dog was going to get Horace and Elias."

Elias put his arm around Mary. They followed the others down the road. Suddenly George pointed ahead. "Isn't that your Pa's wagon?"

"Yes," Mary shouted, "it is!" She ran down the road. "Father! Father! Horace was lost. We found him in the big tree."

Mr. Howe pulled his wagon to a halt. The children climbed in.

"What's this about Horace being lost?" Mr. Howe asked Mary.

Quickly Mary told him what had happened.

Mr. Howe's eyes were serious. "You should have watched Horace more closely," he scolded.

Mary looked as though she was about to start crying all over again.

Elias spoke up. "You're right, Father. We're sorry that we lost Horace."

"Well," Mr. Howe said, "I guess no real harm has been done this time." He leaned over and gave Horace a playful poke. Horace giggled. "I'm just glad you used common sense, Elias. Having Mary throw that meat to the dog was good, quick thinking."

Mr. Howe slapped the reins lightly against the horses. "Now, let's get our new plow."

That night the neighbors came over to watch Mr. Howe put the new plow together. Elias helped. Even his father was surprised at the way

Elias was able to figure out how all parts of the plow fit together.

"You'll make a fine machinist someday, Elias," Mr. Howe said. They gazed at their fine new plow all put together.

The neighbors nodded in agreement. "It is true," they said to one another. "Young Elias Howe does have a way with machines."

A Gift for Aunt Sarah Ann

A MONTH passed. Mr. and Mrs. Howe were very busy getting ready to make the trip for Aunt Sarah Ann's wedding.

"I wish we could go," Mary said the night before they left for Worcester.

"I do too, Mary," her mother said. She looked up from the dress she was sewing and glanced at Elias and Amasa. They sat at the kitchen table doing their homework.

"Elias and Amasa will take good care of you, though," Mrs. Howe said. "George Fisher's aunt said she would look in on you, too. We'll be gone only a day and a night."

Mary frowned. "Horace and the baby are going. Why can't we miss one day of school?"

Mr. Howe came in just in time to hear Mary. "See here, young lady," he said, "it is important to get all the schooling you can." He tickled Mary under the chin. "Besides, think how grown-up you'll feel taking care of yourself for the first time."

"Pshaw!" Mary retorted. "I won't be taking care of myself. Elias and Amasa will be bossing me around, I bet!"

Mr. Howe laughed, but Mrs. Howe looked at him worriedly. "Do you think the children are too young to be left alone?"

Mr. Howe settled down into his big chair by the fireplace. He lighted his pipe. "Amasa is thirteen years old, Polly," he said. "Do you call that too young? Why, it will be only another year before he's out of school and choosing his life's work."

Mrs. Howe nodded and went back to her sewing. "I suppose you're right," she said.

Elias had listened to the conversation with interest. He'd been afraid that Father would decide they were too young to stay alone.

It was going to be exciting taking care of themselves, he thought. Also, they wanted to make Aunt Sarah Ann a wedding present. They had not decided what it would be yet. Elias stared into the fire, wondering what would be a good present.

Mr. Howe cleared his throat. "Finished with your homework, Elias?"

"No, Father." With a sigh, Elias looked down at his schoolbook.

When the three children came home from school the following afternoon, their parents and the two younger children were gone.

"I wonder if they are in Worcester yet," Amasa said. He laid his schoolbooks on the table.

"I guess they are," Elias said. "They left on the early coach."

"I'm hungry," Mary complained. "Let's eat."

"It's only three o'clock," Amasa said.

"Anyway," Elias said, "we've got to think of a present for Aunt Sarah Ann. She and Mr. Haydon will be coming back with Mother and Father. That doesn't give us much time."

They all sat down at the table. Everyone thought and thought, but no one could think of a good present.

"Well," Amasa said, "we know we want it to be something she will see often—something that will make her think of us."

"That's right," Mary said. "Every time she sees it she will know how much we love her."

"It should be something beautiful *and* useful," Elias said.

Mary sighed. "We'll *never* think of a gift that's all those things."

134

"We will if we try," Elias said. He arose. "Let's walk down to Aunt Sarah Ann's new farm. Maybe we'll get an idea there."

"All right," Amasa said. "We better get an idea soon, though. We've got to make the gift tonight."

Amasa and Elias walked down the road. Mary skipped along beside them. When they reached their aunt's farm they walked around the house. They peeked into the windows and explored the barn. They poked their heads into the chicken house. They still couldn't think of a good wedding present for Aunt Sarah Ann.

Suddenly Elias pointed to the weather vane on the barn roof. "That's it!" he shouted.

"What is?" Amasa asked.

Mary shook her red braids. "It's nothing but an old rooster weather vane."

"It does look old," Elias said excitedly. "That's why Aunt would like a new one!"

Elias knew how important a good weather vane was to farm families. He knew it told them when to plant, when to cut hay, when to harvest.

"Wonderful, Elias," Amasa exclaimed. "We'll make her a new wooden weather vane. Let's make a ship weather vane instead of a rooster like that one. I know just how a ship should look."

"All right," Elias said. He knew that Amasa still wanted to be a sailor. Amasa read all he could about the sea and ships.

"I can draw the pattern," Mary chimed in. "You know how good I draw, Elias."

"Mary does draw very well," Elias thought. "Mother said she has talent."

"It's settled then," Amasa said. "I'll tell Mary how the ship weather vane should look. Mary can draw it on that dry, light, pine wood that Father has in the machine shop. Then you, Elias, can cut it with your handsaw and round off the edges on the lathe machine."

Amasa and Mary started off down the road toward the machine shop. Elias didn't follow right away. He stood for a moment looking up at the weather vane on the barn roof. The wood of the vane was cracked and rotted by the weather. "Wooden weather vanes don't last long," he thought. "Maybe we should make our vane out of something else."

Elias ran down the road. He caught up with Amasa and Mary as they were going up to the machine shop. He told them his idea.

Amasa and Mary stared at him. "Whoever heard of a weather vane that wasn't made of wood!" Amasa exclaimed.

"Yes, Elias," Mary said, as they walked into the shop, "Father says that anything else is too heavy to swing evenly with the wind."

Elias sat down on the machine-shop bench. He watched Mary draw the ship on a piece of wood. She used a piece of charcoal. Amasa told her how to make the shape of the ship. "What could we use for the vane instead of wood?" Elias wondered.

All of a sudden Elias sat up straight. He stared at a thin sheet of copper lying on the work table. "Copper!" he shouted. "We'll make it out of copper. Can't you see how beautiful it will look in the sunlight?"

"Don't be silly," Amasa said. "You can't draw a ship on a piece of copper."

"I know it," Elias said excitedly, "but we can use the wooden ship as a pattern. We'll pound the copper to the wooden shape. Then we can take out the wood."

Amasa understood. "The ship will be a light, hollow copper figure!" he cried.

"That would swing easily," Mary exclaimed. "Better than a wooden weather vane even!"

"Yes," Elias said. "It will last a long time too. The weather can't rot it."

Happily the children went to work. They stopped only long enough to eat the sandwiches George Fisher's aunt brought them. They worked far into the night by the light of an oil lamp. At last the weather vane was finished.

"It's beautiful," Mary whispered.

"It sure is," Amasa agreed. "I bet copper weather vanes will become mighty popular with farmers." He looked at Elias. "How do you think up these new things, Elias?"

Elias grinned. "I don't know," he admitted. "It's fun, though."

Mary yawned and said, "I'm tired. Let's get to bed right now."

The boys agreed they were very tired. They laid the weather vane carefully on the work table and went back to the house.

"I hope Aunt Sarah Ann likes our gift," Amasa said, as they got ready for bed.

"I hope so too," Elias said.

"I bet she'll think it's beautiful," Mary said with a deep sigh.

Mary was right. The next day they gave Aunt Sarah Ann the weather vane and her eyes widened with pleasure.

"It's the most wonderful weather vane I've *ever* seen," she declared.

Her new husband, Mr. Haydon, turned it over and over in his hands. "It's a splendid piece of work," he said. "It's practical too. Whoever thought it up?"

"Elias did!" Mary cried. She hopped up and down in front of her aunt. "Do you really like it? Really and truly?"

"Really and truly!" Her aunt smiled. "It's our most beautiful wedding gift."

The children looked at each other happily. Their gift to Aunt Sarah Ann was a success.

A Sailor in
the Family

ELIAS STOOD in the barnyard. He watched down
the lane.

"Are they coming?" Mrs. Howe called from
the kitchen.

"Not yet," Elias answered.

Elias was waiting for Mr. Howe and Amasa.
Now that Amasa was fourteen, he was going to
be a sailor at last. Mr. Howe had taken him to
Boston to sign up as a cabin boy on one of the big
clipper ships.

"How happy Amasa was when he left," Elias
thought. He was glad for his brother, but he felt
sad too. How he would miss Amasa!

"Here they come now," Elias shouted. He could hear the wagon rumbling along the road. Now he could see them. Amasa sat next to Mr. Howe on the high seat.

"I'm going next week, Elias!" Amasa yelled, waving joyfully. "I'm a *sailor!*"

The wagon pulled up beside Elias, and Amasa scrambled down.

Mrs. Howe and Mary came running out.

"Oh, Amasa!" Mrs. Howe cried. She threw her arms around her oldest son. "You're so young to be going to sea!"

"Now, Polly," Mr. Howe said, as he climbed from the wagon, "we can't keep Amasa a baby forever. He has finished school. He is ready to make his own way."

Mrs. Howe wiped her eyes with her apron. She straightened her shoulders. "I'm sorry, Amasa," she said. "I mustn't spoil your last few days at home." She smiled. "Come, everybody.

We'll have the cookies I just baked, and a glass of milk. Amasa can tell us all about his trip to Boston."

The family trooped into the kitchen.

Mrs. Howe served milk and cookies while Elias asked Amasa question after question.

"Whoa!" Amasa laughed. "One at a time!"

Elias smiled. "Sorry, Amasa, but it's so exciting. My own brother sailing all over the world! What kind of ship is it?"

"It's a beautiful ship, Elias." Amasa's eyes sparkled. "Isn't it beautiful, Father?"

"Yes," Mr. Howe said. He sat down beside Amasa. "It's what they call a 'Baltimore Clipper.' These ships are built here in America. They are the fastest in the world."

"What does it look like?" Mary asked. "I've never seen a real ship."

"You ought to see Boston Harbor," Amasa said. "It's full of all kinds of ships."

"Well," Mr. Howe said, "the ship Amasa will be sailing on is very big, of course."

Amasa interrupted excitedly. "She's got three tall masts and huge white sails. Her name is the 'Mary Ann.' Her skipper is Captain Johnson. The captain says that the 'Mary Ann' will easily carry five hundred tons!"

"Yes," Mr. Howe said, "these new-type clipper ships are built to take plenty of weight and still they will travel fast."

Mrs. Howe sat down at the table. "Enough talk about ships. I have an idea. See what you think of it."

Everyone looked expectantly at Mrs. Howe.

"Why don't we have a party for Amasa?" Mrs. Howe said. "He won't leave for a week. That will give us plenty of time. We can invite the uncles and aunts and cousins."

"That's a wonderful idea!" they chorused.

"Would you like that, Amasa?" she asked.

Amasa leaned over. He squeezed his mother's hand. "Yes, I would, Mother," he said softly.

"It's settled then." Mrs. Howe got to her feet. "A week from tonight we'll have Amasa's going-away party!"

The following week was a busy one. Cakes and pies were baked in the brick oven. Notes inviting the guests were sent. Mrs. Howe strung gay lanterns across the barnyard. The long picnic table was taken out of the barn. Everyone helped paint it. They laughed and joked as they worked. This was the last week the family would be together. They all wanted it to be a happy time to remember.

At last the evening of the party came. It was a clear moonlit night. Mr. Peabody, the snow warden, came with his sweet-potato flute. Mr. Jenks came up from the inn with his banjo. Even Mr. McGraw, the schoolmaster, brought his violin.

146

Amasa, Elias, and their parents stood in the
yard greeting the guests.

"There's Cousin Nat," Amasa said.

Elias was shaking hands with old Mr. Philips.
"Where?" he asked.

"Down there. See? He's getting out of Uncle William's coach. Look! There's George Fisher running up to him."

Mrs. Howe smiled. "You boys run along. Your father and I can greet the guests. Boys should enjoy themselves at a party."

"Thanks!" the boys shouted. They raced around the crowd. They ran down the lane to George and Nat.

There was a great deal of grinning and back-slapping as the boys met each other. Then they all fell silent. Nat was the first to speak. "This will be the first summer that we all won't be to-gether," he said.

The other boys nodded unhappily.

Then Elias laughed. "Come on! This is sup-posed to be a party. Listen! Mr. Peabody has started the music."

The boys could see people starting to dance in the light of the full moon.

148

"It's a hoedown," George yelled. "Let's get into the circle."

The boys dashed over to the circle of people. They all joined hands. Old people, young people, boys, girls—everybody danced the New England hoedown!

Mr. Howe stood in front of the dancers. He clapped his hands as they skipped about. He sang out loudly:

> "Dance all night
> Dance a little longer,
> Dance all night
> Dance a little longer,
> Take off your coat
> And throw it in the corner
> Dance all night
> Dance a little lo-ong-er!"

The dance ended with everyone laughing breathlessly.

"More!" they shouted.

Mrs. Howe called, "Refreshments are ready! Everybody come to the table!"

Now everyone forgot about dancing. They rushed to the refreshment table, pushing and shoving good-naturedly to get to the food.

"This is the best party in the world," Amasa said happily. He took a big bite of cake. "I'll always remember it."

"Let's go and sit in the orchard and talk," Elias suggested.

The boys all agreed. They raced around the barn down to the orchard. The moon shot rays of yellow through the treetops.

"Gosh, Amasa," Nat said, "we're sure going to miss you a lot!"

"Yes," George said, "that's what is really hard about growing up. You have to leave all your old friends."

"Just think," Nat said, "Amasa is fourteen already. I'm twelve. Elias and George are eleven.

It won't be long before we'll be going to work too. We might go to the other side of the country. We might never see one another again!"

The boys stared at one another in dismay at such a thought.

"Let's take an oath," Elias said. "An oath to never, never forget one another."

"Yes," George said. "Let's promise that if any one of us ever needs help the rest will come to him as fast as we can."

"No matter *where* we are," Amasa said. He frowned. "Unless of course my ship is in China. I couldn't get here then."

"Wouldn't you try?" George asked.

"Of course I'd try," Amasa said. "I'm not the captain of the ship, though. I couldn't just turn the ship around and come back."

Elias put up his little finger. The boys all hooked their little finger around it.

Elias chanted:

"Friends we'll always be,
Even Amasa across the sea
Will come to help
If—if need be!"

The other boys repeated the oath.

They sat in solemn silence for a moment. Then they heard a giggle. Mary stepped from behind a tree, followed by Horace.

"That sounded silly," Mary said. "Mother sent me to get you, Amasa. Some of the guests are going home. She wants you and Elias to come say good-by to them."

The four boys got to their feet. They looked at each other. The look meant they would keep their oath forever.

Next morning the family was up early. No one said much at breakfast. They felt sad that Amasa was leaving. After breakfast Mr. Howe carried Amasa's big trunk out to the wagon.

152

Everyone hugged Amasa. He climbed up onto the wagon seat beside his father.

"Good-by, Amasa!" they called.

The wagon moved slowly out of the yard.

"Good-by, good-by!" Amasa called back. "Remember our oath, Elias."

"I will, Amasa."

Mrs. Howe and Mary looked as if they were going to cry.

Elias swallowed hard. It wouldn't do for *him* —the big brother now—to cry.

"Good-by, Amasa," he whispered.

The wagon rolled out of sight.

Elias Hires Out

It was a day in early winter. Elias was twelve years old. He hurried out of the schoolhouse and down the road toward home. He was worried about his mother. She had not been feeling well all week. Doctor Allen was supposed to stop by to see her today.

"I hope the doctor didn't find anything really wrong with her," Elias thought anxiously. He turned up the lane toward the house.

"Elias!"

Elias turned at the sound of his father's voice. Mr. Howe was coming down the hill from the machine shop. Elias ran to meet him.

"Is Mother all right?"

Mr. Howe frowned. "No, Elias, she isn't. That's why I wanted to talk to you. I'd rather tell you about it while we are alone."

"What is wrong with Mother?" Elias asked worriedly.

Mr. Howe shook his head. "Doctor Allen doesn't know exactly. He has put her to bed. Next week he is having two Boston doctors come to see her. It will take a good deal of money to get her well, son. We'll all have to help by doing without a few things."

Elias was serious. "I understand, Father," he said. "I'll help any way I can."

"That's a good boy." Mr. Howe put his arm around Elias' shoulder. "Let's not say anything to Mother about how much money these doctors from Boston will cost. Let's be cheerful for her sake, Elias."

"All right, Father," Elias said.

Silently they walked on through the cold air to the house.

All the next week the Howes tried to act cheerful. They tried to pretend that everything was the same as it always had been. It wasn't easy pretending. Mrs. Howe got thinner and paler each day. The doctors from Boston came to see her. When they came out of her bedroom they shook their heads. They spoke in whispers to Mr. Howe, then went away.

"Mother can get well," Mr. Howe told Elias later. "It will take a long time, though. She needs lots of medicine and good care."

Elias knew that his mother's illness would take much more money than they had.

"I could quit school and go to work," he suggested to his father.

Mr. Howe shook his head. "You'll be thirteen soon," he said. "Then you'll have only one more year of school. You must finish."

Later that day Elias told George about it. "So you see," Elias finished, "Father won't let me quit school. I don't really want to leave school. I know how important education is. It's just that I want my mother to get well as fast as she can. The medicine she needs costs a lot of money."

The boys thought for a few minutes.

"Maybe your father would let you hire out," George said at last.

Elias sat up straight. "I never thought of that!" he exclaimed.

Elias knew many boys at school hired out at twelve. They went to live with a farmer who did not have any sons. They helped on his farm before and after school. They were paid each week for the work they did.

"I heard my aunt say that Mr. Flaherty was looking for a boy. He's that old man on the other side of Still Valley."

"The one with the big farm?" Elias asked.

"Isn't he the man that everybody says is stingy and unfriendly?"

"Yes, that's the one," George said.

Elias' heart leaped hopefully. Maybe he *could* help his mother get well. "I'll talk to my father about it tonight," he said.

That night he waited until he and his father were alone in the kitchen. Then he told Mr. Howe about Mr. Flaherty. "He wants a boy to live there this winter," Elias said.

"Hire out?" his father murmured thoughtfully. He looked at Elias' lame leg. "I don't know, Elias. You'll have to do much heavier farm work than you do here. I wouldn't want you to get sick, too."

"Please, Father. At least let me try. I really want to do it!"

Mr. Howe looked at Elias gratefully. "It would help pay Mother's doctor and medicine bills," he admitted.

"I can do it, Father. Really I can. It's only for the winter months anyway. There won't be any plowing or planting or *real* heavy work like that, I'm sure."

Mr. Howe smiled. "All right, Elias. You may go. I'll talk to Mr. Flaherty about it tomorrow. Remember, though, if you are unhappy you come home."

The next day Mr. Howe talked to Mr. Flaherty. It was agreed that Elias would go to live with Mr. Flaherty until spring.

Before Elias left for the farm on the other side of Still Valley, he went into the bedroom to see his mother. The doctors were still keeping her in bed all the time.

Mrs. Howe's eyes were big in her pale face. She smiled gently. "Son, I know why you are going to live with Mr. Flaherty this winter," she said.

Now that Elias was really leaving, he was a

bit scared. He tried not to show it. "I'm going because I want to, Mother," he said.

"No," Mrs. Howe said. "You are doing it for me. You always were a boy who wanted to help others." She gripped Elias' hand. "Be a good boy, son."

"I will, Mother," Elias said.

He hurried from the room. "Mother just *has* to get better," he thought.

Mr. Flaherty's farm was even bigger than Elias had heard. On his first morning there, Elias stood at the window of his attic room. He looked out over the land. The farm was fenced with the stumps of pine trees. The stumps were placed on their sides. The tangled roots stretched out into the air.

"Mr. Flaherty's cows wouldn't dare jump over that fence," Elias thought.

Elias could see all the farm buildings from here too. There was the washhouse where the cleaning woman did the wash. There was a dairy barn with many cows. There was a woodhouse where wood was stored. There was a hoghouse for the hogs. Elias began to feel a little dizzy looking at so many buildings.

"No wonder people say Mr. Flaherty is very rich," Elias thought. "He even has *two* barns for hay." Elias wondered if it was true that Mr. Flaherty expected his hired boy to do the work of three men. George Fisher had told Elias that he had heard folks say that time and time again. Elias hoped it wasn't true.

Elias caught his breath. It was beginning to snow. He'd better get down and gather some wood. He had to start a fire in the fireplace. He had the chickens and hogs to feed too, before he could leave for school.

Mr. Flaherty was already at the table when Elias came downstairs. Miss Welch, the housekeeper, was spooning out the oatmeal.

"Better get to work earlier than this tomorrow morning," Mr. Flaherty said gruffly. "You'll never get your chores done before school if you don't start sooner."

"Yes, sir." Elias sat down. He began to eat quickly. He particularly didn't want to be late for school this morning.

Mr. Flaherty just sat and ate his oatmeal in silence. His bushy black beard bobbed up and down as he chewed.

Elias wished he was home. At home there was laughter and talk around the table at mealtimes. He wanted to say good-by to Mr. Flaherty and leave right now.

Then he thought of his mother. "No," he thought. "I won't go home. I won't give up. Mother needs my help."

The months went by. Elias became more and more unhappy as a hired boy. The work was hard and heavy. Sometimes in school he fell asleep. Mr. McGraw seemed to be scolding him more and more.

Elias never had time for play. Mr. Flaherty didn't believe in play. "I'm paying you to work, boy," he told Elias.

There wasn't any machine shop on the Flaherty farm either. How Elias missed working with machines!

The only time Elias was happy was on Sundays. That was his day off. He went over the meadows to visit his parents. He never told them he was unhappy with Mr. Flaherty. Proudly he gave his father his weekly wages. Each Sunday he was happy to see that his mother seemed just a little bit stronger.

At last spring came. School was over. Elias was going home. How wonderful and free he felt this morning!

He packed his suitcase and went downstairs to the kitchen. As usual, old Mr. Flaherty sat at

the kitchen table eating his oatmeal. As usual, his black beard bobbed up and down. As usual, he nodded at Elias but said nothing.

"I've come to say good-by, Mr. Flaherty," Elias said. "I am going home today."

Mr. Flaherty went on eating.

Elias hesitated. Should he tell Mr. Flaherty he had enjoyed working for him? "No," he thought. "That wouldn't be the truth."

"Well, good-by, sir." Elias turned away.

"Boy!"

Elias turned back. Mr. Flaherty never called him anything but boy.

"Yes, sir?"

"I hear you're interested in machinery."

Elias stared at the old man in surprise. Mr. Flaherty had never asked what he was interested in before. Elias nodded in reply.

"Humph!" Mr. Flaherty muttered. He ate another big spoonful of oatmeal.

Elias shifted from one foot to the other. He wondered if he should leave now.

Then Mr. Flaherty waved his spoon. "There's something for you in the cupboard."

Elias could hardly believe his ears. He went to the cupboard. Inside he found a book. He read the title of the book aloud: *The Young Engineer's Guide.*

"That's right, boy. Written by Oliver Evans. He was an inventor fellow. He died only a few years back."

"He was an inventor?" Elias asked.

"Yup," Mr. Flaherty said. "He invented the high-pressure steam engine. They use them on the new locomotive trains. He was the first engine builder in America too."

Elias had never heard Mr. Flaherty say so much at one time.

Mr. Flaherty pointed to the book. "It's about other fellows' inventions too."

Elias turned the pages of the book. It had many pictures of machines. It showed how the machines were built.

"It's a wonderful book!" Elias exclaimed. "Thank you very much!"

"It's all right," said Mr. Flaherty. "You're a good boy. You worked harder than any boy I ever had. I don't guess it was easy with that lame leg of yours."

Elias felt sorry that he'd ever thought Mr. Flaherty was a mean old man.

"I know you didn't like it here. You didn't give up, though. Wouldn't be surprised if you did something real important someday."

Mr. Flaherty looked at Elias. For a second the boy thought the old man was going to smile.

"Get along home now," Mr. Flaherty said. He went back to eating his oatmeal.

A few minutes later Elias walked over the meadows toward home. He held his new book tightly under his arm. He could hardly wait to get home and read it!

When he got home he found that Mrs. Howe was able to be out of bed.

She smiled at Elias gently. "I'll be well soon, son," she said.

Elias' heart swelled with happiness. All the hard work and loneliness at Mr. Flaherty's had been worth it. His mother was going to get well.

Off to Lowell

ONE SUMMER morning Elias sat in the orchard. He was reading *Young Engineer's Guide*. The book was almost worn out, Elias had read it so many times. He was still very much interested in machines. Ever since he had finished school when he was fourteen, he had wanted more than ever to be an inventor.

"Elias! A letter just came for you!" Fourteen-year-old Mary ran into the orchard. Her pigtails were gone. Her red hair was pulled neatly to the back of her head.

"A letter for me?" Elias reached for the long white envelope. "Maybe it's from Amasa. He hasn't written for a while." Quickly he tore it open and began to read.

"Who is it from, Elias?" Mary asked curiously as he read.

Elias looked up from the letter. His eyes were shining. "It's from Cousin Nat," he said. "He's working at a Lowell textile mill. He says there is plenty of work there. He wants George Fisher and me to come there and work with him."

Mary frowned. "Where would you live, Elias?" she wondered.

Elias looked at the letter. "Nat says that he is living with a friend of his mother's. He says there is plenty of room at her house for George and me."

"I thought that Nat wanted to be a government worker," Mary said. "I remember he always said he wanted to be Governor of Massachusetts when he grew up."

"Still does," Elias said. "He is using the money

he makes at the mill to study law at night school. After he becomes a lawyer he will go into government work."

"Oh!"

"Come on," Elias said. "I want to show this letter to the folks."

Both Mr. and Mrs. Howe read the letter. They looked at each other. Mr. Howe was the first to speak. "You'd really like to go to Lowell, wouldn't you, son?"

"Yes, Father," Elias said seriously. "I think I would be happy working around all those machines and learning all about them."

Mrs. Howe sighed. "I think it best to let him go. He'll never be happy working on a farm. Machines are what he knows and loves."

Mr. Howe looked thoughtful.

Elias held his breath.

"All right, Elias," Mr. Howe finally said. "You may go."

"Yip-pee!" Elias yelled.

He ran to the door. "I'm going to tell George. He'll want to go too."

Mr. and Mrs. Howe stood in the kitchen doorway. They watched Elias run across the fields to George's house.

"I do hope he'll like it in Lowell," Mrs. Howe murmured.

Mr. Howe put his arm around her. "If there are machines there, he will like it."

A month later Elias, George, and Nat were together again. They worked as bobbin boys in the textile mill. Their job was to put the little spools of thread, called bobbins, into the needle-like shuttle.

Elias never grew tired of watching the shuttle weave cloth. The way the shuttle moved in and out made him think of his mother sewing with her needle.

The boys were very happy working at the mill.

172

Then, one day two years later, Nat got some exciting news. A lawyer in Boston wanted Nat to come and work for him.

"You're going, aren't you?" Elias asked.

"Of course," Nat answered. "It's a wonderful chance for me." He looked at his two friends. "I wish you and George could come along with me."

George cleared his throat. "Look," he said, "I wasn't going to say anything about this until next week. Now that Nat is going, though, I might as well tell you."

"Tell us what?" Elias asked.

"I'm going to Boston too."

"You are!" Elias exclaimed.

"Yes," George said. "I have an uncle there. He is a coal and wood merchant. He is getting old. He wants me to learn the business." George laughed. "Don't look so sad, Elias. I want you to come too. Uncle said it would be all right. There will be plenty of work for both of us."

Elias looked uncertain. "I wouldn't want to go into the coal and wood business." Then his face brightened. "Maybe I could get a job in a machine shop there. I could still be near you."

"Of course you could," Nat said. "You are wonderful around machines."

Nat was right. Elias did find work in Boston. He got a job in the shop of Mr. Ari Davis. Mr. Davis was a maker and repairer of machine parts.

Elias was happy to find that Mr. Davis' shop was a meeting place for amateur inventors too. Any time of day an inventor might come in to visit Mr. Davis. As Elias worked, he listened to the inventor talk about his invention.

Elias saw many new things in Boston. One of these things worried him. He passed many small shops on the way to work each morning. In the shops were tailors and seamstresses sewing clothes. He often heard them singing this sad song as they worked:

"With fingers weary and worn,
With eyelids heavy and red,
A woman sat in unwomanly rags,
Plying her needle and thread."

Elias couldn't understand *why* the workers sang so mournfully. One day he asked Mr. Davis to tell him about the song.

"It's called 'The Song of The Shirt,' " Mr. Davis told him.

"Why do the people sing it?" Elias asked. "Why are they so sad? Do they not like to do their work?"

"Well, Elias," Mr. Davis said, "these people are paid for the amount of work they do. They must sew long hours to make enough money to live on. All clothes are sewed by hand. The work piles up until it seems almost impossible for them to sew so many clothes together. They just never get finished."

175

"I see," Elias said. He thought of the slow-moving fingers of the workers. "How wonderful it would be if they had a machine to help them in their work!" he thought. "How much more work they could do every day."

He remembered that long ago his father had said something about such a machine. Elias had never forgotten. Now, as the days went by, he thought about it more and more. How could a sewing machine be made? he asked himself. He *must* find the answer.

Then one afternoon Elias heard an inventor talking to Mr. Davis. He listened closely to what the man was saying.

"I have thought," said the inventor, "to invent a knitting machine."

"A knitting machine!" Mr. Davis exclaimed. "Why not a sewing machine? Goodness knows, the world needs that much more than a knitting machine!"

176

"Impossible!" the inventor snorted. "A needle would have to stitch downward through the cloth. Then it would have to turn around and stitch upward again."

Mr. Davis laughed. "That would be a funny sight, indeed."

Elias glanced up from his work. He saw that Mr. Davis was suddenly serious.

"I don't really think a sewing machine would be impossible to make," Mr. Davis said. "Maybe such a machine would need *two* needles—one above and one below the cloth."

The inventor stared at Mr. Davis. "How in the world would *that* work?"

Mr. Davis smiled. "I don't know. That's up to the inventor to figure out. However, you might be right, my friend. A sewing machine probably would be too difficult to make."

Neither man noticed how carefully teen-age Elias was listening. Neither of them knew that at this very moment his mind was becoming excited by Mr. Davis' words.

"Two needles!" Elias thought. "Two needles working together. It just might work—yes, it just might!"

Then Elias knew he was going to try to invent a sewing machine. It might take all his life, but he was going to try!

Elias Invents the Sewing Machine

It was 1843. Elias was twenty-four years old. He now had a wife and three children to care for. He still worked in Mr. Davis' machine shop. His wages were nine dollars a week.

Elias worked very hard. At night he was so tired he could hardly keep his eyes open. After his family went to bed he would go to his small workroom in his house. He worked on the sewing machine he was building. First he tried to build a sewing machine one way. Then he tried one another way. His machines never worked right. They would not sew.

"If only I weren't so tired," Elias thought. "If

only I had more time to work on my invention. I know I can build a machine that will sew. I know I can!"

Then, tired as he was, Elias would start again to build a new sewing machine. "I will not give up!" he thought. "*Somehow,* a sewing machine that uses two needles instead of one *can* be made to work! I *know* that I can do it if I just try hard enough and long enough!"

Elias' wife became ill. The doctor said she would be sick for a long, long time. Elias had to hire a housekeeper to take care of his children. He had to pay the housekeeper. He had to pay his wife's doctor bills. He had to feed and clothe his children. Nine dollars a week was not enough to pay for so many things.

Elias knew he would have to get an evening job. He would have to work with Mr. Davis in the daytime and work somewhere else at night. It was the only way he would have enough money to support his family. He would have no more time to work on his sewing machine.

Elias was very sad. He did not want to stop work on his invention. He believed that with a little more time he would be able to make his machine work.

Then Elias thought of George and Nat and Amasa. "I will ask my friends to help me solve my problem," Elias said to himself. "That's what I will do."

Elias knew that Amasa's ship would be in Boston by next week. Just this morning he had received a letter from his brother. "I will ask Amasa to go to George's house with me. We'll ask Nat to come too. Maybe the four of us together can plan what I must do," he decided. "I know they will help me."

The next week Elias and Amasa went to see George Fisher. George had become a wealthy coal and wood merchant in Cambridge, Massachusetts. Elias and Amasa decided to stop at Nat's house on the way to Cambridge. Nat was not at home when they got there.

When they arrived at George's house they found that Nat was visiting George. Nat was in politics now. Many people said that they expected Nat Banks to become Governor of Massachusetts someday. Elias was happy that Nat and George were becoming so successful.

The four friends sat in George's living room. The others listened carefully to Elias. He told them about the sewing machine invention. He told them how hard he had been working on it and how impossible it would be to continue.

"I know I can make my machine work," Elias said, "but I am so tired at night that I cannot think clearly. Now my wife is sick. I will have to work night and day to pay the bills. I will not have any time to spend working on my invention from now on."

George was deeply in thought. He scratched his head. "Well, Elias," he said, "I can think of only one thing to do."

Elias looked at his friend hopefully. "What is it, George?" he asked.

"Give up your job with Mr. Davis. Spend all your time inventing a sewing machine."

Elias stared at him. "How can I do that?" he asked. "I have a family to support."

Nat answered. "George is right. You must give up your job with Mr. Davis and spend all your time working on your invention. We will take care of your family. You can return the money to us when you finish your experiments and begin to sell your sewing machine."

Elias looked around at his friends gratefully. "You are willing to take such a chance? The machine I am building may not work. It may take me many years to finally build a sewing machine that sews!"

"Of course we will take the chance," Amasa said. "Friends are always willing to help one another. Remember our oath in the orchard before I went to sea? We believe in you, Elias. We believe you can build a machine that *will* sew. And we want to help you do it."

So it was settled. Elias' friends were to help him support his family while he was inventing his sewing machine.

As Elias walked home that night he thought, "I am very lucky to have three such good friends. I must work very, very hard. I must make my machine a success."

George moved Elias' family into his own house and gave Elias a room for his workshop.

For the next two years Elias worked very hard, indeed. He seldom left his workshop, except to eat and sleep or spend a little time with his wife and children.

By 1845 Elias had, at last, built a machine that

he believed would sew. Above the cloth, the machine had a needle with an eye at the point. This was something no one had ever thought of doing before. All other inventors had tried to build a machine with the ordinary needle which had the eye at the top.

Below the cloth, Elias' machine had a needle to work as a shuttle. Elias remembered well the shuttles he had worked with in Lowell.

Elias called in Amasa, George, and Nat. He wanted them to be the first to see if his machine really worked. The men all gathered around it. Would it sew a continuous stitch? they wondered. Eagerly they watched Elias sit down to run the machine.

Elias put a piece of cloth between the two needles. He reached for the side wheel that ran the machine. He turned the wheel. The two needles *did* work together! They were sewing a tight seam.

186

The men saw that, as the upper needle went through the cloth, an open loop of thread was carried to the underside. Then the shuttlelike needle moved back and forth underneath the cloth and interwove its own threads into the open loop there.

"You've done it, Elias! You've done it!" his friends shouted. "You will be rich and famous one of these days!"

Elias' heart swelled with happiness. "That is good," he said, "but the most important thing to me is that I have done what I have dreamed of doing for so long. I have built a machine that will make people's lives easier."

The men nodded.

Elias looked at them gratefully. He spoke softly. "I could not have done it without you, my good friends."

"We were proud to help you," George said. "Now you must patent your machine. Then you must let people see what a fine machine it is. I am sure everyone will want to buy one."

In 1846, Elias did patent his machine, but not everyone bought one at first. It was too new and different.

"It takes time for people to get used to new things, Elias," Amasa said. "Soon, though, they will see what a timesaving machine it is. Then they will buy it."

"I need money now," Elias said. "I cannot wait any longer."

Amasa looked thoughtful. "My ship is going to England soon," he said. "I will take your machine with me. Maybe the English people will like it and buy it."

Amasa took the machine to London in 1846. Elias waited anxiously to hear from him. Finally he received a letter saying an English manufacturer was interested in the machine. He would pay one thousand dollars for the right to build and sell it in England. He would also employ Elias in his factory.

Elias and Amasa went to London, and soon Elias sent for his family. It seemed that at last his troubles were over. Mr. Thomas, the English manufacturer, did not share the profits on the machine with Elias, though, as he had promised, and in a short time discharged him.

Elias sent his family back to America. He stayed on to try to produce another machine. He was successful. He decided to go back to New York and home where his family was.

Soon after Elias' return, his wife died. He was very sad without her, but he still had his children to care for. He never gave up trying to sell his sewing machine. Little by little, people became interested. By 1856, Elias' machines were selling as fast as they could be manufactured.

Elias was suddenly as rich and famous as his good friends had said he would be. By 1863, his sewing machine was bringing him four thousand dollars a day. He never forgot his own days of hardship, though. He was always ready to help with his money.

During the Civil War, Elias enlisted in the Seventeenth Connecticut Regiment. One day, he overheard the soldiers grumbling because their pay was long overdue. He went quietly to the paymaster and asked how much money was needed to pay the soldiers. The paymaster told him that the amount was thirty-one thousand dollars. Elias gave him a check and told him to pay the soldiers what was owed them. He received twenty-eight dollars for his own back pay as a private.

Elias Howe lived a short but very full life. His health was never very good, but he never let that discourage him from trying to reach his goal.

On October 3, 1867, he died at the home of his daughter Jane in Brooklyn, New York.

Monuments have been erected to his memory. He is one of the few honored in the American Hall of Fame. In 1867 he was awarded the Cross of the Legion of Honor by King Louis III of France. His sewing machine was awarded a gold medal at the Paris Exposition.

Most important of all, though, Elias lived to see his dreams realized. No longer did men and women have to sew every stitch by hand. Elias' sewing machine saved hours of hard labor in both factories and homes.

Today, Elias Howe's sewing machine plays such a great part in everyday life, it is difficult to imagine how the world ever got along without it!

More About This Book

WHEN ELIAS HOWE LIVED

1819   ELIAS HOWE WAS BORN AT SPENCER, MASSA-
        CHUSETTS, JULY 9.

There were twenty-two states in the Union.

James Monroe was President.

The population of the country was about
7,598,100.

1826–   ELIAS ATTENDED SCHOOL AT SPENCER, MASSA-
1831   CHUSETTS.

The first overland expedition to California was
made by Jedediah Smith and seventeen
men, 1826.

Noah Webster published his *American Dic-
tionary of the English Language,* 1828.

Peter Cooper built the first steam locomotive
in the United States, 1830.

1831   ELIAS HIRED OUT TO A FARMER.

Cyrus McCormick invented the reaper, 1831.

Samuel Morse invented the telegraph, 1835.

John Quincy Adams became the first ex-President to serve in Congress, March 4, 1831.

1835   ELIAS WENT TO WORK AT LOWELL, MASSACHUSETTS.

Henry Burden invented a machine to manufacture horseshoes. The machine made most of the horseshoes used by the Union troops during the War Between the States, 1835.

American settlers reached Oregon, 1836.

1840–
1844   ELIAS WORKED FOR ARI DAVIS IN BOSTON AND FIRST EXPERIMENTED IN MAKING A SEWING MACHINE.

John William Draper took the first photograph of the moon, 1840.

Stuart Perry invented a gas engine, using turpentine for fuel, 1844.

1845   ELIAS PERFECTED A SEWING MACHINE.

The Mexican War was fought, 1846-1848.

Gold was discovered in California, 1848.

The War Between the States was fought, 1861-1865.

President Abraham Lincoln was assassinated, 1865.

1867 ELIAS HOWE DIED AT BROOKLYN, NEW YORK, OCTOBER 3.

There were thirty-seven states in the Union.

Andrew Johnson was President, 1865-1869.

The population of the country was about 36,423,590.

DO YOU REMEMBER?

1. What was Uncle Tyler's surprise?
2. What was a bed-patter?
3. How did Elias change the iceboat so it would go faster?
4. How did Mrs. Howe deal with the peddler?
5. What did Uncle William Howe invent?
6. When and where was the first railroad in the United States built?
7. When Elias was eight years old, what did he make up his mind to do?
8. Where did Elias go when he was nine? What unusual thing happened?

9. What was a breaker-picker?

10. What trick did Jocko perform at the fair?

11. When was the cast-iron plow invented?

12. What kind of dance was performed at Amasa's going-away party?

13. What was Amasa's job on the Baltimore clipper?

14. How old was Elias when he hired out?

15. What book did Mr. Flaherty give Elias?

16. What were Elias' wages in 1843?

17. What did Elias do when he learned the soldiers in his regiment hadn't been paid?

IT'S FUN TO LOOK UP THESE THINGS

1. Look up the process used nowadays for preparing cotton for use in making clothes and household necessities.

2. How does a weather vane work?

3. Were special coaches used for carrying mail and freight when Elias was a boy?

4. Who were some other men who invented sewing machines?

5. Where is the American Hall of Fame?

6. Look up the history of the hand-organ, or barrel organ, used by the hurdy-gurdy man.

INTERESTING THINGS YOU CAN DO

1. Bring to class pictures of old Indian burial grounds and Indian relics.
2. Make a map showing Elias' birthplace, where he worked, and where Aunt Sarah Ann was married.
3. Bring to class pictures of old clipper ships. Or, better still, bring a model of one.
4. Find a picture of the French Cross of the Legion of Honor.

OTHER BOOKS YOU MAY ENJOY READING

Cyrus McCormick, Farmer Boy, Lavinia Dobler. Bobbs-Merrill.

Everyday Machines and How They Work, Herman Schneider and Jeanne Bendick, Whittlesley House.

First Transcontinental Railroad, The, Adele Nathan. Trade Edition, Random House. School Edition, Hale.

How and Why Wonder Book of Machines, The,
Jerome Notkin. Grosset.

Simple Machines and How They Work, Elizabeth N.
Sharp. Random House.

What Is a Machine? B. John Syrocki. Benefic Press.

INTERESTING WORDS IN THIS BOOK

backslapping (băk′slăp ĭng) : slapping familiarly or
happily on the back

bobbin (bŏb′ĭn) : spool or reel for holding thread
on a sewing machine or loom

chandelier (shăn dĕ lēr′) : a lighting fixture having
several branches, hanging from the ceiling

charcoal (chär′kōl) : charred or burned wood

clamber (klăm′bĕr) : to climb by catching hold with
hands and feet

clipper (klĭp′ēr) a fast sailing vessel with fine lines,
overhanging bow, tall masts, and large sails

continuous (kŏn tĭn′ů ŭs) : without stopping

darts (därts) : game played with small arrows and
a target

dunce cap (dŭns′ kăp) : cone-shaped hat formerly
worn by pupil for punishment

198

gaze (gāz) : stare intently

good-natured (gŏŏd'nā'tŭrd) : pleasant, kindly, sunny

goggles (gŏg''ls) : large spectacles to protect the eyes

grindstone (grīnd'stōn') : flat, round stone, revolving on an axle, for grinding tools or shaping or smoothing the object

gristmill (grĭst'mĭll') : a mill for grinding grain

handiwork (hăn'dĭ wûrk) : work done with one's hands

handsaw (hănd'sô') : saw used with one hand

hardship (härd'shĭp) : that which is hard to bear

hesitate (hĕz'ĭ tāt) : to be uncertain what to do

hurdy-gurdy (hûr'dĭ gûr'dĭ) : music box played by turning a crank at one side

interweave (ĭn'tĕr wēv) : to weave together

jostle (jŏs 'l) : to run against and push or crowd

lathe (lāth) : a machine in which the work is held and turned while being shaped by a tool

megaphone (mĕg'á fōn) : a large funnel used to magnify sound

overdue (ō'vĕr dū') : not paid at the proper time

porridge (pŏr'ĭj) : broth made of water or milk with ground cereal

quilt (kwĭlt) : bed covering, the top of which is made of small pieces of material sewed together in a pattern, then stitched together with lining and filling

rudder (rŭd'ẽr) : piece of wood or metal hinged on a boat's stern so the boat will turn in the same direction as rudder turns

seamstress (sēm'strĕs) : woman who sews

shuttle (shut''l) : the sliding thread holder in a sewing machine

sprawl (sprôl) : to lie down with arms and legs spread carelessly

sternly (stûrn'ly) : severely, strictly

tailor (tā'lẽr) : one who makes coats and suits

textile (tĕks'tĭl) : pertaining to weaving or to woven fabrics

tiller (tĭl'ẽr) : a lever for turning the rudder from side to side

tinsmith (tĭn'smĭth') : a worker in tin or tin plate

treasure (trĕzh'ẽr) : to value or care for dearly

Childhood

OF FAMOUS AMERICANS

COLONIAL DAYS

JAMES OGLETHORPE, *Parks*
MYLES STANDISH, *Stevenson*
PETER STUYVESANT, *Widdemer*
POCAHONTAS, *Seymour*
PONTIAC, *Peckham*
SQUANTO, *Stevenson*
VIRGINIA DARE, *Stevenson*
WILLIAM BRADFORD, *Smith*
WILLIAM PENN, *Mason*

STRUGGLE for INDEPENDENCE

ANTHONY WAYNE, *Stevenson*
BEN FRANKLIN, *Stevenson*
BETSY ROSS, *Weil*
DAN MORGAN, *Bryant*
ETHAN ALLEN, *Winders*
FRANCIS MARION, *Steele*
GEORGE ROGERS CLARK, *Wilkie*
GEORGE WASHINGTON, *Stevenson*
ISRAEL PUTNAM, *Stevenson*
JOHN PAUL JONES, *Snow*
JOHN SEVIER, *Steele*
MARTHA WASHINGTON, *Wagoner*
MOLLY PITCHER, *Stevenson*
NATHANAEL GREENE, *Peckham*
NATHAN HALE, *Stevenson*
PATRICK HENRY, *Barton*
PAUL REVERE, *Stevenson*
TOM JEFFERSON, *Monsell*

EARLY NATIONAL GROWTH

ABIGAIL ADAMS, *Wagoner*
ALEC HAMILTON, *Higgins*
ANDY JACKSON, *Stevenson*
DAN WEBSTER, *Smith*
DEWITT CLINTON, *Widdemer*
DOLLY MADISON, *Monsell*
ELIAS HOWE, *Corcoran*
ELI WHITNEY, *Snow*
FRANCIS SCOTT KEY, *Stevenson*
HENRY CLAY, *Monsell*
JAMES FENIMORE COOPER, *Winders*
JAMES MONROE, *Widdemer*
JOHN AUDUBON, *Mason*
JOHN JACOB ASTOR, *Anderson*
JOHN MARSHALL, *Monsell*
JOHN QUINCY ADAMS, *Weil*
LUCRETIA MOTT, *Burnett*
MATTHEW CALBRAITH PERRY, *Scharbach*
NANCY HANKS, *Stevenson*
NOAH WEBSTER, *Higgins*
OLIVER HAZARD PERRY, *Long*
RACHAEL JACKSON, *Govan*
ROBERT FULTON, *Henry*
SAMUEL MORSE, *Snow*
SEQUOYAH, *Snow*
STEPHEN DECATUR, *Smith*
STEPHEN FOSTER, *Higgins*
WASHINGTON IRVING, *Widdemer*
ZACH TAYLOR, *Wilkie*

WESTWARD MOVEMENT

BUFFALO BILL, *Stevenson*
DANIEL BOONE, *Stevenson*
DAVY CROCKETT, *Parks*
JED SMITH, *Burt*
JESSIE FREMONT, *Wagoner*
JIM BOWIE, *Winders*
JIM BRIDGER, *Winders*